THE FACE FINDER

MIKHAIL GERASIMOV

THE FACE FINDER

Translated from the German
by Alan Houghton Brodrick

HUTCHINSON OF LONDON

HUTCHINSON & CO (*Publishers*) LTD
178–202 Great Portland Street, London W1

London Melbourne Sydney
Auckland Johannesburg Cape Town
and agencies throughout the world

First published in Great Britain 1971

*This book has been set in Baskerville type, printed in Great Britain
on antique wove paper by Anchor Press, and
bound by Wm. Brendon, both of Tiptree, Essex*

ISBN 0 09 105510 5

Contents

Illustrations

Translator's Preface

The Face Finder is an absorbing autobiography of scientific adventure crowned by remarkable success in several fields.

Professor Gerasimov's book is also unique in that it is the only account available to us in the West of the activities of a Russian anthropologist who is as familiar with the progress of his science outside his own country as within it—he started his career by discovering a most important Old Stone Age site (Mal'ta) in Siberia where he was brought up.

What has been perhaps his most spectacular achievement is the reconstruction of the faces (from their skulls) of unidentified individuals, thus leading to the solution of a number of murder mysteries. In fact, the Gerasimov method of facial reconstitution deserves to be regarded as indispensable for the investigation of certain sorts of crimes.

He has used the same methods for the portraying of a large number of historical characters such as Tamerlane, Ivan the Terrible, Schiller and a Scythian king who lived more than 2000 years ago. He has, in fact, provided history with a new dimension. With the possible exception of Roman portrait-busts we have nothing but idealised pictures of any historical personage before the invention of photography. Gerasimov not only shows us what men looked like but he also tells us about their health or sickness, what they died of and how they moved and held themselves. History in waxworks. . . .

Much of Gerasimov's work has been directed towards the reconstruction of the appearance of early Man, of prehistoric Man, and he has prepared a whole series of such portraits which are undoubtedly the most reliable likenesses of our remote ancestors. Of course, as he himself admits, his task was much more difficult when he came to reconstructing the faces of other men (or pre-hominids maybe) dating from the far distant past. For the fact is that the farther we go back in time the less and less complete becomes the material. Still, what he gives us is of great value.

When dealing with the 'Face of Prehistoric Man' the author mentions that 'recent and revealing finds in Africa have not been taken into account' because detailed descriptions were not available to him, neither had he access to any casts of the material discovered. Gerasimov is here referring to the very significant finds made in East Africa (mostly in Tanzania) from the 1950s onwards.

It may, therefore, be useful for the reader to have some information about these finds, and since further impressive evidence has been forthcoming from another eastern African area (south-western Ethiopia) as recently as 1968 (and could therefore not have been mentioned by the author in any case) I have added some account of the Omo Valley discoveries. They concern Man at both ends of his pedigree—from the australopithecine stage to that of *Homo sapiens*. In this way the author's presentation may be amplified without any attempt being made to modify his conclusions. The early story of Man is so complicated and the evidence for it still so scanty that there must be, perhaps for a fairly long time, some divergence of view about details, although the main lines of the story are clear enough.

It is now rather generally accepted that Man is a tool-making animal and that a creature which walked upright and resembled however coarsely what we could recognise as a 'human being' is not entitled to the name of Man unless he could and did make tools. Thus a cultural factor is introduced into the criterion. The difficulty, of course, is how to determine that any given type did or did not make tools. It is claimed that some hands of fossil specimens which otherwise would be classed as, let us say, 'pre-hominids' are of such a formation that they could not chip a pebble precisely enough to produce a cutting edge.

However, the earliest man-made stone implements appear in equatorial Africa in the Lower Pleistocene period, and at that time there may have been several sorts of primitive hominids evolving at once.

The Australopithecine type was first recognised in South Africa in 1924. Since then australopithecine remains have been recovered from various parts of Africa as well as from the Levant. These remote ancestors of ours included creatures very like apes as well as others with a number of features which are man-like. And some of them do not seem to have made tools while others did so.

It can now (1970) be regarded as most probable that the early forerunners of our kind were African Primates of a sort whose later (but not most evolved) representatives were found in South Africa, and since the most abundant remains of them have been found in the Transvaal, we may deal with these first. Can they count as Men? Probably not, anyway as tool-makers.

In the South African sites where the remains only of *Australopithecus* and *Paranthropus* (the two main types of *Australopithecines* of South Africa) were located; no artefacts, no tools have been found. But at, for instance, one site (Sterkfontein Extension) it is clear that the cave-mouth was occupied by a group of tool-making creatures. Were these a superior sort of Australopithecine who ate their own kind or were they a more advanced sort of hominid—formerly called *Telanthropus* and now generally recognised as a pithecanthropoid form under the name of *Homo erectus capensis* whose remains have also been found at the site and who may have been the first South African tool-maker who ate Australopithecines? It is indeed possible that at one period there were in South Africa three sorts of primitive man-like creatures.

In any case the Australopithecines of South African seem to have been a conservative lot who survived until comparatively late times in the southern African cul-de-sac isolated from the north by an enlarged Kalahari Desert extending farther eastwards than it does at present.

It seems certain that the 'home' of the Australopithecines, their 'differentiation area', lay much farther to the north.

The most ancient australopithecine material, indeed, was recovered from the Omo Valley by the International Research Expedition in 1967–8. This valley extends for some 200 miles along the lower course of the Omo river which empties into Lake Rudolf. The valley is filled with comparatively recent deposits of gravels and loose material in which fossils are preserved rather well. The area has been known for some time as one rich in fossils, but it is wild country infested with bandits and it was with the protection of Kenyan and Ethiopian guards—the territory lies wholly in Ethiopia—that the Expedition conducted its fruitful campaigns in 1967 and 1968.

The French contingent of the Expedition unearthed the half of a lower jaw and a complete lower jaw (with most of the teeth in place): both specimens were of a robust type of Australopithecine and seem to be far more ancient than any others known—the K/A (potassium-argon) dating for both mandibles ranges from 2·37 to 2·56 million years.

The Chicago contingent of the Expedition recovered a number of australopithecine teeth which in size and shape are comparable with those from two sorts of Australopithecines *(africanus* and *robustus)* from South Africa.

Since the material is so fragmentary it is difficult to say just what was the type/types of the Omo Australopithecines, but they can be dated with some certainty to the Pliocene-Pleistocene border. In fact this Omo material may push back our pedigree to a dating nearly 3 million years ago.

And it would seem that at least two sorts of Australopithecine were living in the Omo area at the same time.

As the evidence piles up it looks as though there were several sorts of hominidae or 'pre-men' existing in Villafranchian times (that is in the earlier part of the Pleistocene). What are called 'adaptive radiations' are familiar in the early stages of a group's evolution and if such 'radiation' holds good for the hominidae in Villafranchian times then it would not be surprising to find, say, *Paranthropus* earlier than *Australopithecus* in some areas and later in others—such are the complications of palaeontology.

All this may seem not very enlightening and indeed rather obscure, but the most exciting evidence is just that which Gerasimov was unable to appreciate, and it comes mainly from the now famous site of the Ofduvai Gorge (Tanzania) which is a curious canyon some 300 feet deep whose stratified sides reveal fossiliferous beds extending right down to the impermeable basaltic bed-rock. The whole consists of deposits laid down by a lake. The lowest bed of the strata (with many fossils) has been dated rather vaguely to as much as 2 million or to rather less than 1 million years. In any case the next bed above may represent the deposits of some 400,000 years.

In 1957 there were found in Bed 1 portions of a skull associated with 'pebble-tools' (i.e. very primitive artefacts made by chipping pebbles to an edge) and the broken bones of many animals—evidently the remains of meals. The skull, which could be fairly well reconstructed (it was found in many fragments), was that of a youth aged about eighteen or nineteen. It was furnished with a very strongly marked 'sagittal crest', that is a prominent ridge running along the middle of the skull from back to front. This curious feature was almost as much developed as in some gorillas. The specimen was at first dubbed *Zinjanthropus boisei* but is now recognised as a species of Australopithecine.

Further exploration of Bed 1 revealed hominid bones at a rather lower level than the 'Zinjanthropus'—foot and hand bones, parts of a skull and a lower jaw. These appeared also to belong to a kind of Australopithecine which some would call *Australopithecus habilis* (i.e. tool-maker).

But from Bed 2 the remains of yet another type of hominid (and therefore thousands of years, maybe hundreds of thousands of years, later in date than 'Zinjanthropus') were recovered, about whose classification a good deal of discussion has taken place. This *Homo habilis* of Bed 2 has jaws that in shape are rather hominine than australopithecine, and it may be that this *Homo habilis* is specifically of the same type as the South African 'Telanthropus' (see above), in other words a pithecanthropoid form.

On the face of it, then, it looks as though there were two main lines of Australopithecines—one we may call *Australopithecus habilis* (i.e. a tool-making Australopithecine) that merged into *Homo erectus* (i.e. a pithecanthropoid form) and another type which was cut off in southern Africa and survived (in at least two main sorts) as tool-users (but not makers) and scavengers.

At least that is what the evidence looks like at the present time. It is a pity Gerasimov could not give us a reconstruction of 'Zinjanthropus': he must have been a forbidding kind of individual.

The other most recent material relating to our pedigree comes also from the Omo Valley, but it is evidence so many tens of thousands of years later than the Omo Australopithecines that it seems almost modern, indeed it relates to 'modern' Man almost indistinguishable or quite indistinguishable from ourselves.

The history of *Homo sapiens* is even more puzzling than that of other types of Man.

Until a generation or so ago the view was current that men of our kind, 'recent' Man, appeared 'suddenly' in western Europe in the middle of the last or Würm Ice Age, say 35,000 years ago, and displaced the Neanderthaloids who just as 'suddenly' disappeared. But where these *homines sapientes* came from no one could guess.

Then it became apparent that types like *Homo sapiens* (and unlike, for instance, the Neanderthaloids) had existed in Europe long before the last Ice Age, but none of these people's remains is complete. None of the facial bones of the Swanscombe (England), Fontéchavade (France) or Vertesszölles (Hungary) have been preserved and, of course, without these it is impossible to say just how like *Homo sapiens* these ancient men were. What we can say is that in the parts we possess these ancient Europeans' heads might pass for the skulls of some sort of 'modern' Man of our own kind.

Now (1967–8), however, from that same Omo Valley where have been unearthed what seem to be the oldest remains of Australopithecines have also been recovered what appear to be the most ancient specimens of *Homo sapiens*. It is tempting to speculate on what was the population-history of the Omo Valley region during the many hundreds of thousands of years which elapsed between the time of the Omo Australopithecines and the 'modern' men's era of only a few tens of thousands of years ago. Were the former the distant ancestors of the latter? That is to say was a specimen slice of human evolution provided by the banks of the Omo river? No, most probably not, but the course of our ancestry did run very probably somewhere in the region of east equatorial Africa.

The Omo *sapiens* skulls are four in number, three of which are in fairly good condition. Omo II has a nearly intact cranium minus the facial bones, whereas Omo I is not so well preserved, but some of the all-important face-bones as well as a fairly complete lower jaw were found, so that the form of the face can be or could be reconstituted—it is a pity that Gerasimov could not set to work on this Omo Man. The only feature in these skulls which strikes one as being rather exceptional in a *Homo sapiens* is the very broad neck of Omo I, but the head of Omo II tapers to the neck region in typical *sapiens* fashion. It is possible to say that this

Omo II can be paralleled among what are undoubtedly 'modern' or' recent' men.

With the skulls were discovered portions of other bones—those of the arm, the leg, the spinal column, etc.—and none of these differs from what would be regarded as normal among *Homo sapiens*.

These Omo modern men's bones contain no more radiocarbon, so they must be dated back to a period before 40,000 or indeed before 45,000 years ago. Have we here evidence for the existence of early *Homines sapientes* somewhere near their homeland? Anyway, not only the hominids as a whole but our own sort of *Homo* also would seem to be African animals.

Perhaps the above may help the reader to supplement with some recent evidence the story Professor Gerasimov tells in so striking a fashion, concerning his reconstructions of the heads of prehistoric Man. It is clear that we cannot expect the portraits of men of the remote past to be as instructive as those of men of historic times—the material the author has had to work on is often far from complete. But Gerasimov's remarkable and indeed astonishing success in 'finding faces', in reconstituting heads from skulls, in indicating the identity of unknown persons, proves abundantly the reliability of his methods.

Finally I have to add that Professor Gerasimov died aged 62 in July 1970, after this translation had gone to press.

A.H.B.

Author's Introduction

For countless generations men have endeavoured to throw some light into the darkness of the past and the urge to know what lies behind us is especially strong when it comes to investigating Man's origins and to trying to find out what 'early Man' looked like. However, in this age of scientific progress our knowledge of the origins of Man and of the development of the most ancient cultures can only be described as very patchy. New discoveries very often fail to offer us the hoped-for explanations but these discoveries do force us to re-examine theories and classifications which have come to be taken for granted. The fact is that Man's very ancient story is an extremely complicated one and the material we have at our disposal does not allow us to present that story without a good many gaps.

Not less complicated is the problem of how Man has arisen from his pre-hominid forbears. For very long periods, often for many tens of thousands or even hundreds of thousands of years, we have only two or three specimens (sometimes in the form of isolated pieces of bone) to serve us as documents. So our knowledge of the details of evolutionary trends is still rather vague.

Even in those rare cases where a relatively complete set of skeletal material has been brought to light we are often presented with fantastic descriptions of the outward appearance of the men whose bones we have. Many were the attempts—the unsatisfactory attempts—to reconstruct the appearance of most ancient Man. We may mention the first work of the Jena anatomist Schaaffhausen (1877) and the experiments of the two Swiss, Kollmann, the anatomist, and Büchli, the sculptor, who reproduced the physiognomy of a woman from the epoch of the pile-dwellings (1899).

This last production was the first really scientific reconstruction in the sense that Kollmann and Büchli proceeded from researches that had been methodically conducted. Kollmann, for instance, measured the thickness of the soft part of a hundred women from the Auvergne region of France and proposed a definite technical procedure for reconstructing heads and faces from skulls. In this way he produced a scheme for the head and this was 'corrected' and 'enlivened' by Büchli—he furnished the nose, mouth, ears and hair. Despite the interference of the sculptor, Kollmann's work can rank as one of the most remarkable achievements in the history of scientifically based reconstructions of heads and faces from skulls.

Later on other anatomists and anthropologists made further attempts. Many portraits were prepared from the skulls of Pithecanthropoids, Neanderthaloids and men of the Late Old Stone Age. We may mention some of them since it cannot be denied that they had some claim to scientific objectivity since they were all based, more or less, on morphological data.

Thus in 1910 the anatomist Solger, using as a starting-point the skull of the neanderthaloid youth from the Le Moustier cave, constructed the head of an adult of the same type. In 1913 the anthropologist Martin and the anatomist Eggeling (a professor at Jena University) constructed, independently of one another, but from one and the same skull (that of La Chapelle-aux-Saints), two very different portraits of Neanderthaloids.

At about the same time Louis Masquet (a talented sculptor who was guided by the Belgian anthropologist Rutot) modelled a series of portraits of early Man. These reproductions were, at the time, greatly admired, although they can hardly rank as scientific documents.

Undoubtedly the head of the La Chapelle-aux-Saints Neanderthaloid as reconstructed by the French anthropologist Marcellin Boule must be mentioned as a most interesting piece of work. Boule reproduced from the skull only the muscular tissues of the head, face and neck with no indication of skin covering. This skull was, later on, utilised by many others, among them the American anthropologist MacGregor, the Russian anatomist Bystrov and the Polish anthropologist Midljarski, as the basis for neanderthaloid portraits which, however, even in the main features of the type, differed widely from one another.

Attempts to represent the outward appearance of fossil Man have, therefore, been undertaken repeatedly over a long term of years, but since the favourite subject was the La Chapelle-aux-Saints specimen and, as I have said, each reconstruction differed widely from the others, doubts about the authenticity of all were aroused and the reconstitution of a human physiognomy from a skull was discredited.

Admittedly during the last century there appeared a number of works with pictures of skulls of well-known persons together with portraits of these same persons painted during their lifetimes. A number of anatomists impressed by these illustrations came to the conclusion that there existed an unmistakable correlation between the living face and the facial skeleton which allowed an identity to be proved without any doubt. Thus, by comparing a self-portrait by Raphael with the skull of the artist (Raphael's tomb was opened in 1833) the anatomist Welcker demonstrated that the skull was indeed authentic.

The anatomist Geiss identified the skeletons of Bach, Kant, Haydn and others. In this connection the reader may be interested in the story of the Bach monument set up in Leipzig in 1908. The grave of Johann Sebastian Bach (1685–1750) was discovered at Leipzig in 1894. Geiss compared the skull from the grave with portraits of Bach painted during his lifetime and demonstrated that the skull really was that of the composer. Fourteen years later the German sculptor Sefner while working on the Bach monument utilised not only portraits but also the contour of Bach's skull. From a plaster cast he modelled the soft parts of the head using the same technique Kollmann had recommended in his day. The reconstructed head was then checked with the portraits. As might have been expected this reasonable method resulted in an extremely precise likeness for the Johann Sebastian Bach monument.

But Sefner was not satisfied, he wanted to prove experimentally that a close connection existed between skull shape and head-face form, in other words what he wished to produce was proof that from a given skull only one portrait can be produced, namely that of its own particular visage. His experiment was significant enough. He took a cast of the Bach skull and attempted to reproduce from it the head of the composer Handel. He succeeded in doing this, but only by disregarding the size and shape of the skull. The reconstructed head was much too big, so that in places the soft parts were merged into the bone structure while in other places they had to be thickened abnormally in defiance of all the rules of anatomy.

Sefner's experimental method found no imitators. It was a good deal later that the British biometrical school developed a complicated system for proving the identity of skulls from portraits. By the use of this method Welcker and Giess were proved correct in their identification of the Raphael, Bach, Kant, Handel and many other skulls. Indeed, with the help of this method many skulls of historical personages were recognised.

Again, extensive use was made of a simplified method of superimposing photographs of living persons on those of skulls—and this method proved of value in forensic medicine . . . all this should have been enough to show that a close connection existed between the form of the skull and the soft parts of the head and face. Nevertheless anatomists and anthropologists were almost all unanimous that reconstructions of a physiognomy from a skull could not rank as authentic. To find the reason for this let us go back to the history of the problem.

Here, perhaps, we may recall, first of all, an ill-fated attempt to reconstruct a face from the skull of a contemporary woman. Professor Eggeling of Jena University conducted for a number of years some very interesting observations on the variations in thickness of the soft parts of heads and faces. He worked out a technique of measurements and collected an abundant material. From this the thickness of the soft parts at various points of the head and face could be determined. Test reconstructions of faces from skulls showed that with this technique portraits representing a racial type could be modelled. But Eggeling was not satisfied with this result and in 1913 he proceeded to a well thought out and prepared test.

He took a plaster cast of the head of a recently deceased man and measured, in accordance with a definite plan, the thickness of the soft parts at various points so that with these craniometrical data the soft parts of the subject could be modelled. Then the skull was freed of its soft parts and two plaster casts of it prepared. The casts and the data regarding the soft parts were given to two sculptors who working independently were to model from the casts the portrait of a man unknown to them. Eggeling, of course, expected that the sculptors working in similar conditions would each produce a similar portrait of one and the same person. But the results were completely unexpected. The reproductions showed no likeness either to each other or to the original.

This experiment led Eggeling and also most anatomists to the conclusion that no individualised portrait could be constructed from a skull. However, today it can be maintained with certainty that the failure of this noteworthy test was due to the carelessness or the lack of conscientiousness of the two artists. They did not observe the all-important preliminary conditions for the success of the experiment, namely paying great attention to the correlation between shape of the skull and thickness of the soft parts.

The number of very differing representations produced by various persons from one and the same skull and the failure of the Eggeling experiment resulted in many scientists regarding the idea of reconstruction as fundamentally false. The fiasco of Eggeling's test has not yet been forgotten though it occurred over half a century ago.

The Czech scientist V. Suk, the greatest adversary, wrote in a polemical article 'Error of anthropological identification and reconstruction' (1935) that a series of special investigations had proved that the reconstruction of the face from the skull, especially the modelling of the nose and mouth, was impossible. He declared that the soft parts certainly did not correspond to shape and form of the underlying cartilage and still less to that of the bone . . . 'Consequently the findings of osteology and anatomy allow us to conclude that Man can be examined and explored only when the soft parts are present. All the fossil remains of Man which have come down to us are in the form of skeletal bones and can be investigated only as skeletons which can offer us no clues at all for any reconstruction that is true to life.'

Thus, according to the opinion of the majority of anatomists and anthropologists, neither the reconstruction of the outward appearance of recent Man (as far as an individualised portrait is concerned), nor the reconstitution of fossil hominid forms, rank as authentic.

The reader will not find in this book any detailed discussion about the justification for the work of reconstructing the appearance of Man from his bones. Not words but concrete examples will show that reconstructions of recent Man have proved the reliability of the method in crime detection.

During recent years many of the reconstructed portraits I have prepared from skulls have become well known, have been reproduced in scientific and popular literature and exhibited in various museums. Information about test reconstructions will be offered so that the likeness of the reconstructions will be demonstrated by means of photographs of the subjects when living.

Attempts have sometimes been made to attribute to some personal talent of mine, and especially to some phenomenally developed sensitivity, the resemblance of reconstructions from skulls with photographs of their owners. All this is certainly very flattering for me but it does not correspond to the facts. The success of my students in the use of methods proposed by me is proof enough that in their main lines they are the right ones. My students not only fashion portraits of Stone Age or Bronze Age men but they also regularly undertake tasks for the identifying of unknown persons. They have not only made their own the reconstruction methods recommended by me but also in co-operation they have completed these methods and with the aid of a rich factual material have in many respects refined my methods.

The reader will not, I think, expect from us any description of the various phases of the reconstruction of the face from the skull. This work is not a textbook intended for teaching purposes, therefore we only describe the method briefly. The main purpose of the illustrations is to give graphic evidence for the reconstruction of heads from skulls.

From this introduction it may be seen that the idea of the reconstruction of the face from the skull arose in connection with the problem of Man's origins. During forty years of work I have created over 200 reconstructions of Man's face belonging to various epochs. Here, I can, of course, select only the most significant and important.

The main part of the book consists of documentary portraits of historical personages. In a succession of short, self-contained sections are reported the searches, the excavations and the actual work on the portraits. The sections do not follow chronologically according to the dates of the persons concerned but they appear in the order in which the portraits were made. In this way, I think, the development of the method is most strikingly illustrated and the reader persuaded of the increasing reliability of the reconstructed portraits.

M. GERASIMOV

1 *From Skull to Visage*

How it all began

Time and again when I have been giving lectures to audiences of many different kinds, or when I have been in conversation with members of other professions than mine, I have been asked why and how I began to work on the problem of reconstructing faces from skulls. What was it that had urged me on to such an unusual activity? How long had I been engaged in it? Who had my teachers been?

In fact I would often put these same questions to myself when I tried to remember the real cause of my ever-increasing interest in the appearance of early Man, and in his life and in prehistory generally. And I can find no straightforward answer.

No one in my family took any interest in archaeology, palaeontology or even in geology. My father collected butterflies and postage stamps. He was also a keen fisherman. My mother liked painting and going to the theatre. I cannot recall anyone mentioning primitive Man.

But I would like to set everything down in chronological order. I was born in St. Petersburg (now Leningrad) in the year 1907. My father was a doctor. In those days many new settlements were being established in eastern Siberia and the Far East. The Trans-Siberian railway had just been completed and at the big junctions were formed what were known as 'transit stations', that is to say 'colonies'.

From 1912 onwards my father was chief medical officer in one of these settlements adjoining the town of Irkutsk. My whole childhood and youth were, then, linked with a suburb of this city. When we arrived the building of the settlement was just about finished. To it was allocated a large area of virgin forest and this tract of country began on the edge of a high terrace through which cut a wide depression. Along the bottom of the depression gurgled the water from a small lake in the terrace, which was covered with a thick mixed forest. On either side of the glen there grew luxuriantly briars, mountain-ash, black alder and wild rosemary. On the terrace itself a narrow path led through the woods and ran between the hospital hutments and the administrative building. The trees pushed so close to the walls that they shrouded the houses. A little farther on there was the great forest with all its splendours. There were masses of mushrooms and various sorts of small game. In my early childhood days I was then in close contact with nature. I learned to read at a very early age and when I could not be out-of-doors I would sit hour after hour pouring over a fine illustrated edition of *Universe and Mankind*. The usual boy's games meant nothing to me. What excited me most were books of travel and exploration. Later on my own 'explorations' were devoted to the search for 'antidiluvian' animals—and men. I was the eldest child of the family—my brothers and sister had other interests and played with children of their own age.

I had hardly gained a certain amount of freedom for my rambles when my amusements caused real trouble in the household. Stones and animal bones piled up in the children's room, where I had installed my museum. I can well remember how bitterly I cried when I was forbidden to take into the house a trophy of which I was very proud. It was a horses' skull complete with all the teeth. I was only a little over five at the time and could not understand why a nice, clean, white horse skull would not be an ornament to the room. I do not know how things would have turned out if my father had not found a solution.

Near the house was an old shed with windows. Part of it served for storing the hospital archives, but I got most of it for my museum. At first the animal corner occupied a very special place in this room—aquaria and terraria, an aviary and animal's cages. When, however, a little tame squirrel came to grief, I no longer had the heart to keep creatures in prison, so my museum changed its character.

Quite early on I was not only familiar with the bone structure of many animals but I also studied the human skeleton. I learned how to gut beasts, to prepare them, to stuff them, and at the same time to mount skeletons. I would see in a skeleton not only the bony framework of, say, a mouse or a mole, but also a fossil creature. My childish fancy knew no limits and now and then I would construct marvellous beasts made up from parts of different skeletons. I can remember one monster composed of a big toad's body and a chicken's head. But the most daring creation was a portentous one formed from the bones of a cat and a duck. The cat's skull was set at the end of a long neck (the duck's backbones) while the body and legs came from the duck and the hind legs and the tail from the cat. This monstrosity for long mounted guard over my museum. The fantastic combination of bones struck all beholders with astonishment.

I did not go to school until I was eight since it was far from the settlement and I would have to walk at least three miles. The subject for one of my first school essays was 'What would you like to become?' I wrote I would like to be an archaeologist and, like Georges Cuvier, would model the outward appearance of living creatures from their bones . . . not only those of animals but of early Man.

So even as a ten-year-old boy I expressed just what would be my future activities. In fact I defined the aim of my life. Shortly after this I read about the work of Kollmann and Büchli in Switzerland. They had constructed the bust of a neolithic woman. I also learned about the Belgians, Louis Masquet and Rutot who had prepared a whole series of portraits of primitive Man.

Then, too, I read how Schiller's 'right' skull had been found (see pp. 181 and 183) and at first did not believe what I read. I learned about the Schiller skull from a paper by A. Kalitinski 'On the Reconstruction of the Physiognomy from the Skull' in which was a detailed description of the discussion that had gone on for years about the matter. The conclusion was that Froriep had found the real Schiller cranium. All its measurements coincided with those of the poet's terra-cotta death-mask.

I knew very well that clay shrinks when dried and still more when baked, therefore the terra-cotta mask's measurements could not correspond to those of the skull, but must be a good deal smaller. So the cranium in question could not be Schiller's. These various publications gave me an idea of the way many scientists conducted their researches and I realised that in order to pursue such researches myself I must not only be a skilled anatomist but also adept in modelling and drawing.

There was at Irkutsk an art studio run by the painter Ivan Kopylov. He was a first-class teacher and knew me well since I had taken drawing-lessons from him at school. My maternal grandfather (Sergei Viatkin) was a painter and had graduated from the St. Petersburg Academy of Arts. It was my mother's dream that I also should become an artist, so when she noticed my interest in sketching she took me to see Kopylov. But even my mother's urging could not shake him. He would not take me and declared categorically that it would be a crime as well as a waste of time to let me study sculpture and painting since I had not the slightest talent. So I remained without any special artistic education.

However, I did sketch a good deal both with pencil and pen and I modelled in plastics. But what I represented was not what I saw but always what I imagined . . . for instance, fossil animals, dinosaurs, lizards, mammoths and so forth.

The country around Irkutsk is exceedingly rich in pre- and proto-historical finds. On the banks of the Angara and its tributaries are numerous sites and graves dating from the Neolithic and early Iron Age. The arable land held a superabundance of pottery fragments and kitchen middens. Extensive areas of the clayey soil contained a rich late Pleistocene fauna.

So, from the first spring days when the snows began to melt, through the whole summer and a good part of the autumn, I spent much of my time on enthralling archaeological adventures. In winter I devoted all my spare moments to working on my collection of treasures. The objects were catalogued, numbered, restored and prepared for exhibition since my trophies developed into a regular museum. On the shelves lay animal fossils—bones and teeth of mammoth, a skull and the long bones of a woolly rhinoceros, fragments of bison and horse skulls, stags' and elks' antlers. Sewn on to sheets of cardboard were fragments of Neolithic and Iron Age pottery. There were boxes full of many flint flakes chipped by Old Stone Age men and a number of microliths in various stones, beautiful little jasper, chalcedony and flint arrowheads, large leaf-shaped javelins together with scrapers, borers, splendid choppers and chisels in nephrite and other stones. On the walls hung drawings of mammoth, rhinoceros and other prehistoric animals.

Then came my first real archaeological excavations. I was lucky enough to discover, in a breach of the terrace alongside the

Angara, a number of disturbed neolithic graves. With meticulous care I gathered up all the bone fragments and for months on end busied myself with the restoration of damaged skulls and portions of skeletons. These first attempts at restoration not only gave me great satisfaction but also forced me to be most orderly and thorough in the work.

Besides the human remains the grave contained pieces of stone artefacts, smashed bones and damaged clay pots. I have said that the settlement area on which we lived gave directly on to a high terrace. During the construction of the railway embankment, part of the terrace edge was cut away so that a large slice was exposed. In the whole section thus laid bare finds of fossil fauna were very frequent. At one spot, at a depth of about 1½ metres (59 inches) I came upon a mammoth's tusk, in very bad condition, it is true, and near it the splinters of another animal's ribs.

So here it was that as a ten-year-old boy I began my first excavation. Day after day, and month after month, I dug and I dug until I had disengaged a mammoth's tusk and two teeth of the upper jaw. There were also some mammoth ribs and bones of other beasts and finally a retouched flint undoubtedly the work of Man. What excitement! I was on the track of primitive Man, the contemporary of the mammoth.

All the animal remains and the implements were carefully drawn and described. Though the bones were in a poor condition, they were put out of harm's way and came into my museum. At this spot I went on digging, but farther down there was nothing more to be discovered. So obviously I had to enlarge the dig at the side. For more than an hour I burrowed my way farther and farther into the ground. Then, as I was tired, I stopped and sat down, then I heard something like the sound of sand trickling, at first quite softly . . . then louder and louder . . . I stumbled instinctively towards the opening—and the next minute the earth broke over me. I felt a tremendous weight, but between my face and the surface of the soil was a slight vent of air. I felt no anxiety but I had no hope of ever getting out. I could not move a finger. Then as the burden became insupportable my senses sank into confusion.

I have no idea how long I lay in the earth. I had begun to dig about eight o'clock in the morning and the landslide must have happened about ten. I did not recover consciousness until the evening and then I was lying in my bed at home. Some peasants on their way back from market had dug me out. I was told that one of them had noticed a leg sticking out of the ground. After they had got me free they were a long time before they discovered whose child I was . . . so my career as an archaeologist almost ended before it had begun—so to speak.

Here I would like to tell of an episode during my childhood; it was an adventure which, I think, powerfully influenced my attitude to nature and to men.

Some time before our family had come to settle in Irkutsk my father was driving in the middle of the night not far from the Siberian town of Nerchinsk. He was on his way to visit a patient . . . suddenly through his half-slumber he heard the howl of wolves. Then a shot rang out followed by calls for help. Father at once was fully awake and said to the driver, 'What was that, Feodor? It seems someone is calling for help. Pull in the horses.' Feodor turned round a terrified face . . . 'Yes, Doctor, someone is calling out . . . we must help him.' Then he urged on the horses through bush and brake towards the spot from where the cries came. In a couple of minutes' time my father saw in a thick patch of wood a man kneeling and facing a sitting semi-circle of waiting wolves. The horses would not budge an inch farther. Father began to shout. Feodor let out a terrific yell. The wolves shambled back most unwillingly but not far enough. Feodor could hardly hold his horses. Father ran over to the man who by now had fainted.

He was a Tungus hunter. Later he told us how he had been followed by the wolves for over three hours. He had killed several and had escaped for a short time—then the wolves were behind him again. He sped off into the thickness of the forest. Then he broke one of his skis on a tree-stump hidden by the snow. He felt a very sharp pain in his leg. The wolves were now quite near. He had used his last cartridge and was preparing to resign himself to his fate when shots and cries resounded. After that he knew nothing more.

Father diagnosed a severe double fracture of the lower left leg.

Both bones were broken, muscles and blood-vessels torn. The Tungus had lost a lot of blood. For more than two months he had to lie in bed at our house. The leg got well, and the hunter—his name was Joasaf—left us, but from then onwards every second year, just after Christmas, he would turn up again. Although his nomad's settlement was on the middle course of the Chilka river—that is to say at least 1000 kilometres (over 600 miles) away he would come on his skis to visit us and would stay about a week in my father's study. Then he would disappear for another two years. For me Joasaf's visits were festive occasions.

He was an old man of low stature and most dignified though good-tempered. His small screwed-up eyes were always laughing. This man of the taiga, who could neither read nor write, possessed astounding delicacy of feeling. He was pleased with everything and spoiled us children immeasurably. He would bring us all sorts of presents, little things he had fashioned himself—whistles, bird-calls, model traps and so forth. For Father there was always a big hunk of smoked bear's meat. Joasaf would sit by the fire quietly puffing on the long, thin mouthpiece of his little Chinese pipe. But his hands were always busy. He would twist a thread out of a fine tendon, or would repair his clothes, or would whittle out of horn or bone some small object of hunting-gear known only to himself. For hours at a time I would sit bemused and stare at his delicate, nimble hands.

Sometimes he would lay his work aside and select a birchwood log, rip off its bark and then without leaving hold of his knife would, rapidly and dexterously, cut out silhouettes of animals—reindeer, elks, bears, wolves, etc. They were so true to life and so artistically executed that they not only delighted us children but also grown-up people.

I was now in my twelfth year and was growing into a strong, well-built lad. The continual archaeological researches and the wanderings had hardened me. I was a tireless walker and feared neither wind nor weather. That year Joasaf came to us rather earlier than usual and he stayed three days. Then he told my father he wanted to show me the taiga, that is the dense rather marshy forest of Siberia. He had got everything ready. On a light arctic sledge he had brought all the necessary gear—from cap and mittens to broad, short skis and a knife. It did not take long to get ready and we set off with everything we needed for two months. It was January and there were 40° centigrade of frost.

How my father and mother ever allowed me to go passes my comprehension even to this day. But I lack words to express how thankful I am to old Joasaf. I still do not know exactly where we went, probably somewhere in the foothills of the Baikal area.

During our whole journey we came across no villages, we did not meet even a single human being and in those six weeks Jaosaf taught me a very great deal. I learned how to make a fire in any weather, how to build a forest hut, how to find wood in the taiga. Joasaf never killed a bird or any other creature unnecessarily, nor did he wantonly break a twig or branch. In his view trees, animals and stones all had souls. He used to say 'all men want to live'. He taught me in fact to see the life of the great woods and to live there without fear.

I have never to this day forgotten the lore of the old Tungus.

The year after this adventure we got a new natural-history teacher at our school. She was called Liubov Petri and was not only an understanding teacher but a marvellous human being who formed a club of young natural-history students. She soon noticed my keen interest in archaeology and palaeontology. After about a month she invited me to her house and introduced me to her husband, Bernhard Petri, who had the chair of archaeology and ethnography at Irkutsk University.

Now a new phase of my life began. I was an active member of the student circle for local lore and culture and I began to feel at home in the Archaeological and Ethnographical Institute. My particular job was the preparation of the collections. And at that time I had a first meeting with Georgie Debez, then a student at Irkutsk University. About two years later I made the acquaintance of Alexei Okladnikov. The already mentioned circle was in close contact with the museum for local culture and with the geographical society. So I developed as a pupil in the company of archaeologists, ethnographers, historians and zoologists who were members of the East Siberian Geographical Society.

Contact with important researchers, teachers and professors of Irkutsk University and medical school did much to help me enlarge my range of vision. My direct teachers and masters were Professors Petri (archaeologist and ethnographer), Dorogostaiski (a zoologist), Bushmakin and Grigoriev (physicians). It is to them more than to any others that I owe thanks for the results I eventually obtained, although none of them was concerned with the problem of reconstructing faces from skulls. They provided when I was still very young the foundations which were to make possible a regularly organised and correctly conceived plan of research.

My speciality is palaeontology. For this I was trained and to this I have devoted most of my professional activity for many years. My great interest has always lain in the earlier phases of Man's history. But, at the same time, I have constantly been engaged with the problem of reconstructing the face from the skull.

Since the foundation of the Laboratory for Plastic Reconstruction at the Ethnographical Institute of the U.S.S.R. Academy of Sciences (in 1950) I have devoted myself especially to documentary reconstruction and to the elaboration and development of a method for reconstructing faces from skulls.

2 *First Faltering Steps*

It was in the autumn of 1920 that for the first time I took in my hands a skull with the definite object of reproducing from it the face of a man unknown to me. I had at that time a clear idea of the position of the main face and neck muscles, but, all the same, I was assailed by numerous problems. How could the shape of the nose be determined? How should the mouth appear? How should the eyelids and eyebrows be shown? . . . and there were many others.

None of the numerous anatomy atlases could provide answers to these questions. The muscles of the head were shown too schematically and too vaguely. The publications I had at my disposal contained only slight, and, indeed, often contradictory, information about the thickness of the soft parts. I saw quite clearly that without a course of special training I would never be able to reconstruct a face from its skull.

Thanks to my acquaintances in medical circles I had at this time access to the anatomical museum and the dissection rooms of the university medical high school. For several months I attended lectures on anatomy and forensic medicine and at the same time I worked with groups of students. But even then I did not get very far. Obviously what I needed was a quite different programme of study, since I had by now realised I must discover the elements of the face-skull correlation, that is to say I must discover on the skull the morphological clues for the reconstituting of the details of the face.

As soon as I had realised this I ventured to consult the holder of the chair of forensic medicine, Professor A. D. Grigoriev, an original man of great experience. His lectures were always lively and interesting especially when he was engaged in practical demonstrations of dissection. He had the extraordinary faculty of seeing everything, of judging acutely and of remembering what he had seen. The diagnoses in his forensic medicine reports furnished astonishingly exact and complete descriptions.

He was mild-mannered, friendly and patient with everyone even if in his attitude towards young people he might display a touch of irony as though he were slightly amused. But the only things he would never tolerate were boasting and lying, they enraged him and he would become distant and even harsh while he pinned down a lie pitilessly. So although his students feared him a little, they liked him all the same since they thought him very just.

Alexander Grigoriev knew me quite well although I was too young to become one of his regular students, but since he noticed I never missed one of his lectures or practical demonstrations he did all the same consider me as a student. So he was not surprised when one day I asked to speak to him privately though what I had to say was unexpected.

My first question was . . . 'Professor, do you think it possible to make an authentic reconstruction of the face from the skull of a contemporary man?' He answered unhesitatingly, 'Yes, I am persuaded that it is possible, colleague, but doubtless you know that all attempts to do this have hitherto been unsuccessful. Why? Because, in my opinion, something has not been taken into account in the examination of the morphology of the face. Obviously the programme followed hitherto has not been the right one and the reconstruction technique has not been accurate enough.' Then he added: 'But perhaps you will try your hand at this very interesting task? However, you must realise that in this matter I can, practically speaking, be of no help at all.'

Then I ventured to say that I needed some experimental material on which to work. Alexander Grigoriev smiled and said, 'All right, you shall have some, but first of all you must draw up a detailed programme of work. You don't want just to chop off heads anyhow!'

So the matter was settled. A month later I was in possession of the measurements Kollmann had elaborated as the fundamental indications for determining the thickness of the soft parts of the head. The essence of the programme was that not only definite information about the thickness of the soft parts must be found but also morphological features of the skull which could serve as clues for the reconstruction of the different parts of the face—nose, mouth, eyes and so forth.

From the relevant literature and my own observations I knew that the soft parts of the head and face were not everywhere alike. They varied indeed very much from place to place. But would there not be some areas of the head and face where they varied less, that is to say are constant? Naturally the measurements must always be taken at the same point and this must be easy to find on both head and skull.

I felt my own head and realised that the soft parts on the plane of the profile did lie closest to the skull-bone. The soft parts thickness varied just as little on a line running through the lower margin of the eye-sockets, the middle of the cheek-bones and the upper margin of the auditory meatus, that is the eye-ear plane.

Now the profile points had to be fixed. (1) The most projecting part of the back of the head. (2) The upper part of the parietal bones. (3) The upper margin of the forehead. (4) The middle of the forehead. (5) The glabella, that is the middle of the supra-orbitary region. (6) The root of the nose. (7) The middle of the nasal bones. (8) The end of the nasal bones. (9) The deepest point on the lower margin of the nasal opening. (10) The cleft of the chin. (11) The most projecting point of the chin. (12) The lowest point on the contour of the chin. Also must be taken into account the height of the upper lip from point (9) to the mouth opening, the total thickness of the mouth, that is to say of both lips.

At first I measured each head before the corpse was handed over to the students. Very soon, however, I realised that the thickness of the soft parts varied much even on the main planes.

The scope of this book does not allow for a description of the work in all its complexity.

Two years went by since I had begun working under the direction of Professor Grigoriev. Yet, it was only after two years of stubborn labour that I dared proceed to a reconstruction and this not only from modesty but from prudence. I remembered well enough Eggeling's failures and I was afraid that if a similar misfortune befell me Grigoriev would lose interest and without his continued support I would be unable to achieve anything more.

My first attempt at a reconstruction I showed to no one and indeed soon destroyed it. In so doing I discovered numberless mistakes, some due to technical insufficiency and some to the unsuitability of the plastic material employed. For almost six months I experimented in order to produce a waxen mastic which perfectly suited my purpose.

In 1924 I modelled the head from the skull of a Buriat and at the beginning of the next year two more heads respectively of a Chinese and a Tungus. All three heads displayed clearly the features of their racial type and in addition showed a certain individuality, that is to say they were not just schematic but indisputably portraits. But this was, nevertheless, just our impression which could not be confirmed since no likenesses of these men existed.

I considered that there was no special merit in producing the appearance of a typical Chinese or European when the type of skull was evident. Therefore I began thinking about a complicated experiment to produce an individual portrait from a skull whose whole head had been photographed. It was not until about the end of 1925 that I was able to put my plan into execution. I received the skull of a man unknown to me. But after careful examination I came to the conclusion that it was of a girl aged at most sixteen to seventeen years. It was a wonderfully harmonious skull with a steep forehead, narrow face, beautiful teeth, delicate lower jaw and elegant but markedly prominent chin. The rounded eye-sockets with thin margins were very large, the cranial symphyses not yet occluded and the third molar not yet erupted. Such features were enough to determine sex and age. The reconstructed head proved to be very good-looking and what was much more important a really true portrait.

In 1925 I was appointed scientific technical assistant in the Irkutsk Museum and from 1927 to 1930 I was in charge of its archaeological section. These were years of intensive archaeological exploration, research and excavation. In 1926 appeared my first publication devoted to a palaeolithic site I had discovered on the territory of the settlement.

In the years 1926 and 1927 I modelled heads of fossil Man. One from the *Pithecanthropus erectus* skull of Dubois (the skull had been reconstructed by Weinert) and the other from the neaderthaloid Man from La Chapelle-aux-Saints. My God, what naive productions these were! When I looked at my lamentable Pithecanthropus and Neanderthaloid I realised quite clearly that my knowledge of the morphology of the face even of recent Man was not sufficient for a correct solution of my task although a true-to-life reconstruction of fossil Man's appearance was certainly possible. But I kept in mind that one could not hope to produce an authentic reproduction of the most ancient forms of Man as long as one did not know how to reproduce the individual portrait of a recent man.

On 11th March 1928 I got a letter from the librarian A. Beltram at the village of Mal'ta telling me that a peasant called Platon Brilin had discovered a bone so large that three children could sit on it and use it as a toboggan down the slopes.

Although it was freezing hard I set off for Mal'ta in order to inspect the fossil. It turned out that the bone came from a huge mammoth and had been dug up by the peasant while he was building a house. For twenty-four hours I had a fire burning in the hole so that the earth thawed out and even then I could clear a space of only about a square yard. I found the remains of a cultural level. In this small space I found fragments of reindeer antlers, the teeth and ribs of a rhinoceros, splinters of mammoth tusks and teeth, many bones of arctic fox and half the skeleton of a huge wolverine. There were also many split bone, pieces of charcoal and reworked flint artefacts.

Thus was discovered one of the most ancient and rich of eastern Siberian Upper Palaeolithic sites. I named the site after the neighbouring village—Mal'ta.

Now began many years of systematic excavation at this extraordinarily well-preserved legacy of fossil Man. Remains of dwellings in good condition, many artefacts, an immense number of artistic representations as well as models of birds, animals and even men were dug out. These excavations were to occupy me for a long time, but in the winter months I carried on steadily with my work in the mortuary and in the dissecting rooms of the medical high school, though I made no reconstructions. But I collected material and it was in those days that I noted a number of very noteworthy peculiarities. The human face is, whether beautiful or ugly, always harmonious. And this is why we at once notice traces of cosmetic interference or of plastic surgery operations. An asymmetry of the face corresponds to an asymmetry of the skull. Certain features of the skull's construction, which allow of a true-to-life reproduction of facial details, can be recognised.

The sensational results of three years' research in palaeolithic Man's hunting settlement at Mal'ta led to my being invited to attend the International Congress for Quaternary Geology in Leningrad.

And in Leningrad I remained at the Academy of Material Culture in the special section for archaeology and anthropology. Here my work on the problem of facial reconstruction from skulls received a new impetus and took on new forms. This was quite natural, since I was meeting new men, able men with very definite ideas.

But at the same time as I came up against the inexorable and hostile scepticism of some of my older colleagues I also enjoyed the practical and friendly support of some anatomists and anthropologists—and I felt the astonished curiosity of laymen. All this increased my energy for work and I determined to run a considerable risk. Since test experiments aroused general attention I felt no more anxiety about failure—that was just unthinkable. But this did not mean I was immune from mistakes and small blunders. They were unavoidable but I was fully persuaded that the reconstruction of faces from skulls was possible . . . I knew that the problem had been solved essentially.

Trustworthiness of Reconstruction

The first test reconstruction of a girl's head (1925) was carried out quite objectively, that is to say I knew absolutely nothing about the skull and still less about the face. But the experiment was still not sufficiently supported by documentary evidence. So it convinced no one but myself. Officially I had not yet the right to assume that reconstruction of faces from skulls was possible at all.

Since my work was still only in its early phase, it found but little acceptance. My obstinate determination to carry on was mostly attributed to mania and fanaticism. But in any case I did not meet with indifference on my way. What these varied and indeed contradictory attitudes to my work did induce was self-criticism in my appreciation of what I was doing, so that now, at last, I dared to consider that the first part of the problem was solved, that is to say that an individual portrait can be based on a skull and be so true to nature that an individual unknown to me could be identified and recognised by his relations and friends.

So let us look back to the beginning of the 'thirties when I resumed my activities in Leningrad, when a series of tests was conducted under the watchful eyes of my colleagues. They would be able to clear up the question as to whether with my method different racial types could be reproduced from skulls.

For these experiments three skulls were chosen from the anthropological museum of the U.S.S.R. Academy of Sciences. I knew nothing about these skulls, though I could see that they differed very considerably from one another. One of them showed a number of features typical of peoples from equatorial regions. The second was obviously that of a Mongoloid, while the third was of an Europoid. To begin with only the left-hand side of the faces was to be reconstructed, the right side was to be left uncovered for possible verification. Independently of the racial type, nose, mouth, eyes and ears were reproduced according to the individual indications of the skulls. In this way heads with definitely marked racial features were produced. The first skull proved to be that of a Papuan which was confirmed by the description in the museum catalogue. The second skull was that of a Kasakh and showed scarcely perceptible traces of europoid influence (but as the skull came from an Orthodox churchyard it probably belonged to a hybrid). The third skull showed a marked resemblance to a Khevsur head and indeed it came from a Caucasian of the Khevsur highlands.

Although I had not paid special attention to it, the age of the specimens was clearly indicated and the reconstructed heads showed symptoms of age which corresponded perfectly with the biological age of the persons in question. This experiment did convince my colleagues that facial reconstruction from skulls could not only give correctly the main features of a racial type but also an individual resemblance to a living person.

The next series of tests should show that, in addition to what had been achieved, a portrait reconstruction was possible. By this we mean that so close an approximation to the appearance of a living person could be obtained that even an unknown individual could be identified.

M. M. Gerasimov working on the skeleton of Ivan the Terrible.

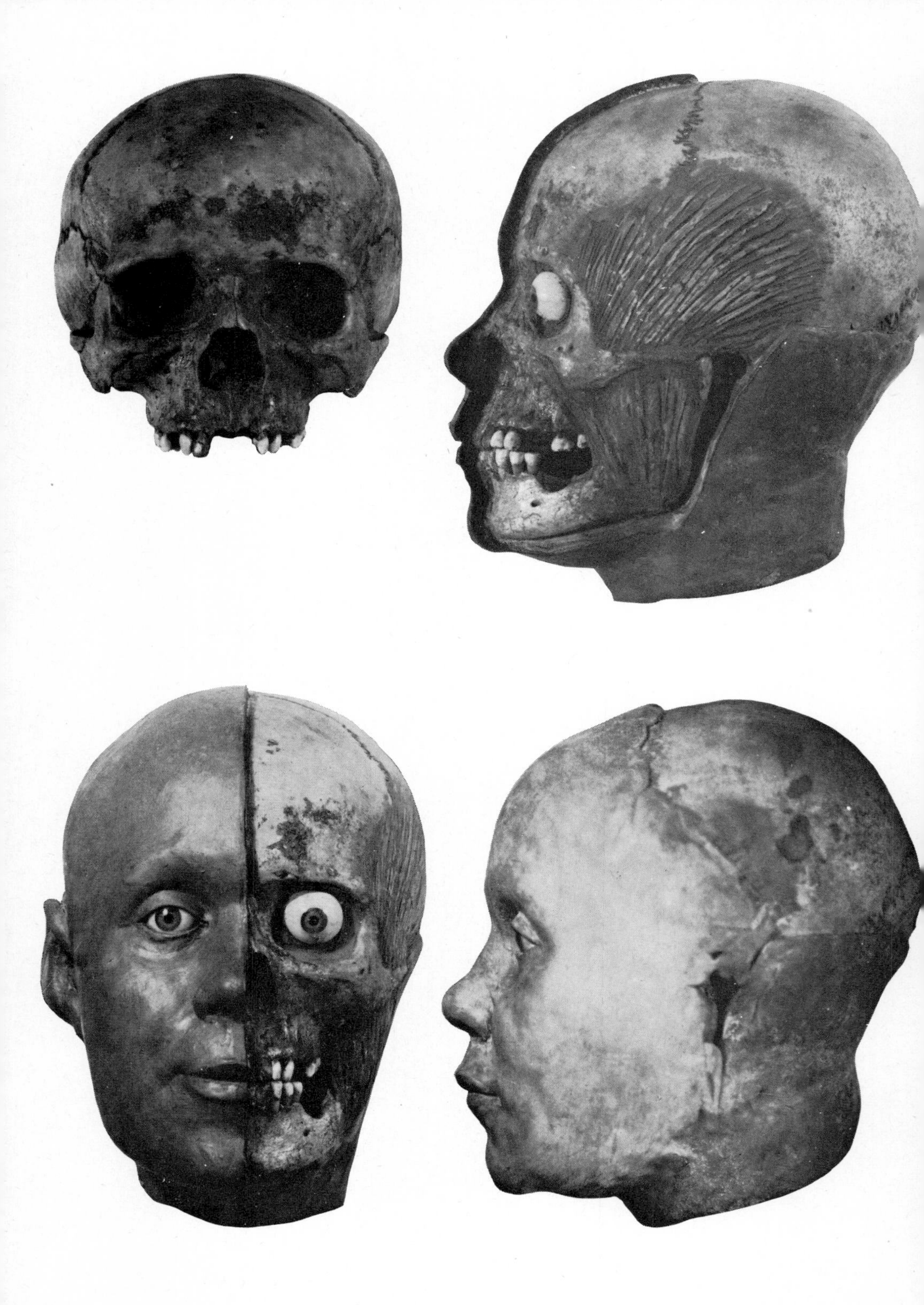

In the case of Valentina Kosova who suddenly disappeared a few days before she was expecting the birth of her first child, a skull lacking the lower jaw (*opposite page above left*) was submitted as evidence for identification. The reconstruction of the head (*opposite page above right and below right and left*) presented a face with well-marked forehead prominences, rather small eyes, a snub nose with a slightly undulating profile, and a regularly formed mouth. The comparison of the completed reconstruction (*above left*) with a photograph of Valentina – taken six years before her disappearance – (*above right*) showed so great a resemblance between them that her remains were identified and her murderer convicted.

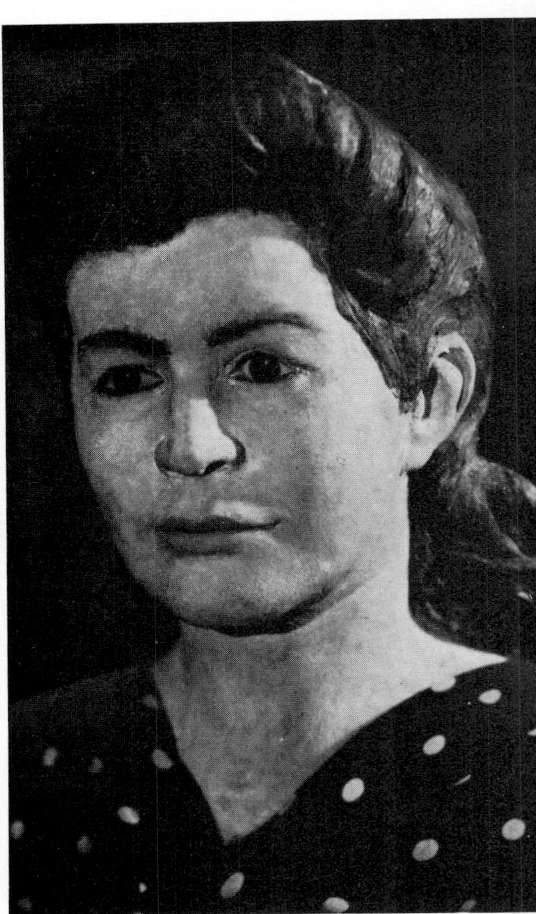

The comparison of the finished reconstitution (*above right*) with a photograph of the missing dentist Nina Z. (*above left*) showed a surprising likeness which was especially noticeable in the asymmetry of the eyes.

To this problem I devoted myself during much of the time between 1934 to 1940. Quite unexpectedly, however, an obstacle arose in my path. There was in the research and academic institutions no 'known' skull, that is to say one which could be attributed to definite persons. Very few skulls indeed could be identified by photographs or pictures. Skulls which were guaranteed by pictorial documents came often from persons whose facial reconstruction no one would consider as objective since the portraits of these men and their description were known far and wide, e.g. the skull of the writer Turgeniev.

After a great deal of trouble, however, something in this matter was achieved. In 1935 I happened to find in the third medical high school the skeleton of a man unknown to me, but it bore his name and I was told that his relations possessed photographs of him taken in the last years of his life. A better opportunity could not be wished for. The skull was handed over to me and I set to work. The reconstruction presented the head of a man about forty years of age. The face was unprepossessing, it had a very high, narrow forehead, a long and projecting nose, deep-set little eyes, a full mouth, a large receding chin and protruding ears. The lips, however, were slightly smiling and lent the whole visage a surprising charm. The portrait was clearly a success and of this I soon convinced myself when I was able to examine a number of photographs from a family album. I was able to meet the mother of the man in question, and as the portrait pleased her so much, I was deeply moved and made her a present of it. Such was the story of Dr. Kolesnikov's portrait.

The Likeness of the athlete Loustalot

About six months later I once more had the luck to receive the skull of a known person. It came from the skeleton of a Frenchman, Loustalot, and was preserved in the 'Lesgaft' sports high school in Leningrad. Loustalot was a very accomplished athlete—swimmer, boxer, gymnast and fencer. In his time he was one of the first to swim the English Channel. Later he lived for a number of years in Russia and was for long instructor in boxing and fencing at the Lesgaft school. I knew that not only his skeleton but also his death-mask was preserved, so the experiment would be especially valuable. But a bitter disappointment awaited me. I wanted to make this reconstruction as graphic as possible. So I reconstructed the masticatory muscles, modelled the soft parts but built up only the left half of the face. That was enough to enable me to compare my work with the death-mask and show how the portrait was copied. When I had finished I went to the Anatomical Institute where the Loustalot death-mask was kept. Teachers and students gathered around me and looked expectantly at the result of the experiment.

There was the Loustalot mask, but I could hardly believe my eyes. The portrait I had produced was very different from the mask. Only the forehead and the twice-broken nose were identical and proved that I really had used Loustalot's skull as my model. But the whole of the lower part of the face was different and I would say even alien—strange. The face was noticeably broader, as though bloated. The blurred eyes projecting from their orbits and the swollen mouth with thick, shapeless lips were quite unlike those of the face modelled by me.

Nevertheless, the face I had reconstructed was lean and rather delicate, with strongly marked muscular relief, in fact the typical face of a Frenchman no longer young; it was undoubtedly good-looking, expressive and showed determination.

So, the experiment was an obvious failure. My disappointed audience melted away. Still, baffled as I was I could not make up my mind to destroy the work that had cost me so much trouble.

Several days passed. The Loustalot portrait stood on a cupboard. The energetic profile stood out strikingly against the white wall. One evening a friend of my wife, Olga Orlova, came into the room. When she had glanced at the new reconstitution she moved over closer to it and then burst out: 'That must be Loustalot . . . isn't it? But why without his moustache and a quite different hair-cut?'

I was puzzled. Olga Orlova had been one of Loustalot's pupils and had known him well. So now I wanted to convince myself that Olga was right. I was very keen to submit my experiment to further proof.

Then I discovered that a large number of Loustalot's former

pupils were working in the Leningrad foundation for scientific and technical films, so I went to see the director and described my unfortunate experience to him. He had indeed with him a number of pupils who had attended the Lesgaft high school. I asked him if he would summon these nine to him, one by one. They should look at the reconstructed head and say if they recognised it. So as to prevent any collusion between them, not one of them should leave the director's office until all the nine had given their opinion.

All of them, independently, recognised Loustalot's head, but all the same they remarked on the lack of a moustache and declared that the hair-cut was different from Loustalot's. None of those questioned could imagine that the head of their teacher had been reconstructed from the skull and that I had made my model without ever having seen Loustalot. So my method got a tardy confirmation.

But where was the error? Why was Loustalot's death-mask so unlike my reconstruction? There was an explanation. Loustalot had died suddenly at an advanced age. He fell dead as he was waiting at a tramway halt. As he had no papers on him, his body lay for a considerable time in the mortuary before it was identified. He was not reported missing for several days. Then a search was made for him and when he was found his face was already so disfigured as to be unrecognisable; however, a death-mask was made all the same.

More years passed by . . . the hard times of the world war were over. Then by chance I saw in the illustrated paper *Ogoniok* a small illustration showing a wrestling match. Under the picture was the caption 'Loustalot teaching his son jiu-jitsu' . . . and then I was fully convinced that my Loustalot portrait had been a success.

The Portrait of a Papuan

Gradually, with test experiments, my technical method of facial reconstruction from the skull became increasingly refined. I now proceeded to generalise all the information obtained, that is to say combine it so as to form a definite methodical foundation for my theory. In this way what is usually called a 'hunch' developed little by little into a science. Naturally I kept anatomists and anthropologists informed of my researches, so that I might receive not only agreement and assistance but also critical judgements about my work . . . I simply could not imagine how one could proceed other than collectively.

Once, it was at the beginning of 1937, I gave a lecture on my tests and presented a number of heads, among them the portraits of Dr. Kolesnikov and of Loustalot. In the hall were professors and students from the Anthropological Institute of the Moscow State University. I counted on a discussion since I had for the first time sought to describe the basic principles for the reconstruction of faces from skulls. What I advanced was of unequal validity. Together with concrete observations and factual data there was much that was still hypothetical, and it was only my test-reconstructions themselves which gave proof of the validity of the main thesis of my speech. But contrary to my expectations, there was no scientific discussion about my statements. On the contrary, a number of the most outstanding anthropologists of the day expressed their mistrust concerning what I had said and the reconstruction I had presented.

I ended my discourse in dead silence. Then I proposed to conduct a test experiment in the presence of my sceptical listeners—and they themselves should select the skull. 'Are you suggesting we should keep watch over you for two months?' came a loud and distinct voice from the back rows. I kept my temper—with some difficulty I admit—and replied mildly, 'Oh, no, I will take only two hours of your time, if as much.' This answer, which I delivered with an appearance of complete calm, made an unexpected impression. The whole audience remained silent. Then someone—I do not know who it was, maybe the chairman, Mark Plisezki, the director of the Anthropological Institute himself—proposed that the experiment should take place the next morning.

I was so excited that I hardly slept the whole night. I cursed myself for having been so hasty—all the more because I usually took ten days for a test reconstruction. When I had copied a face I then checked the basic measurements before destroying what I had done and beginning all over again. If in both cases the same head appeared then all was in order. In this case, however, it was a matter of finishing off the work in two hours, and it had to be faultless. Otherwise all was lost and no one would take the trouble to check off where my error lay. A failure would serve as a proof that a facial reconstruction from a skull is just not possible. More than twelve years' work would at one swoop be revealed as vain.

At about nine o'clock I was at the Institute and half an hour later everyone who was to test my work had arrived. They were all leading anthropologists. Only two of them showed any sympathy for my work and even they were critically inclined. I can, however, not forbear from thanking G. F. Debez and Y. Y. Roginski. They reassured me by their support, although I allowed nothing to appear of my excitement and seemed quite self-possessed—if they had only known what an effort this cost me!

In a small room some plastilin was prepared and soon the skull was produced. I had expected anything, but not what I saw. My colleagues so 'well disposed' towards me had set me a pretty task. The skull was clearly not Mongoloid, nor was it Europoid, but apparently Negroid. The skull vault was long, narrow and high, the forehead steep with a strongly developed supraorbital region, the root of the nose was depressed, the nasal bones were markedly projecting, the nasal aperture very wide, the eye-orbits large, the face comparatively narrow and very prognathous. The large teeth were blackened, obviously from betel-chewing, the chin was broad and not very projecting.

So, all right. What I had before me was an equatorial type unknown to me. Instinctively doubts arose in my mind. Was I capable of undertaking this experiment? Did my whole method depend on researches made with two great races, the Mongoloid and the Europoid? I remembered that according to Birkner the thickness of the soft parts in Negroids differed from that in Mongoloids and Europoids. But was that right? I had myself never had occasion to check this statement. I had never dealt with Negroids and had never even seen X-ray photographs of any. But there was no turning back now. So I set to work. All the time there were two or three people in the room—sometimes more. They observed closely, they relieved each other, they came and they went. But I hardly noticed them. All my attention was fixed on the job. I had no time to measure meticulously the soft parts to be reconstructed or to check the work by repeated reconstructions. So I modelled purely by eye and as things came up. I reconstructed the large masticatory muscles, and from them came the shape of the face and the contour of the cheeks. Then a median line was drawn over the whole head. That determined the profile. On the vault of a skull the thickness of the soft parts does not vary much, it is very much the same from the back of the head to the supraorbital area. In this case, however, the latter region was so strongly developed that the thickness of the soft parts must there be greater. The root of the nose was deeply depressed but since the nasal bones jutted forwards the basal profile was also to be reconstructed as projecting and the lips were made full as befitted the large incisors and the general prognathism of the face. After that eyeballs were placed in the orbits and then the soft parts covering the vault of the skull and the facial bones were modelled in accordance with the usual 'normal' standards. The ears were represented schematically as was the hair. The job was finished. I had built up half a face in one hour and forty minutes. Very shortly afterwards I could compare my work with the death-mask of the individual.

The mask was remarkable, of coloured wax with plentiful, natural hair and furnished with ornaments which had belonged to the person in his lifetime—around the forehead a richly ornamented band of small slabs of mother-of-pearl, in the nose was a boar's tusk, the lobes of the ears pendant from the insertion of bone ear-rings. A small beard completed the picture. It was the head of a Papuan.

Although the hair I had represented on my reconstruction differed from that of the mask and although I had put no hair on the face or boar's tusk through the nose, the likeness between my reconstitution and the death-mask was unmistakable.

But despite this once more the voice of an unconvinced sceptic was raised: 'Hm . . . of course the reconstructed head does look like the original, but then it is only the head of a Papuan, and all Papuans look alike just as the Chinese do . . . as alike as one egg is to another . . . yes . . . if you were to reconstruct the completely recognisable portrait of an individual . . . why, then . . .'

The sceptic had forgotten that a few days before the close likeness of my portrait of Dr. Kolesnikov to photographs of him had been demonstrated. My theoretical antagonist had not been able to appreciate that I had rather surprisingly succeeded in reproducing the face and appearance of a man belonging to a race unknown to me. But, in any case, my proposed method was proved to be fundamentally correct so that by utilising it the portrait of any man could be modelled, irrespective of what his race might be. The recognition of this fact implied also that not only *Homo sapiens* and recent Man in the strictest sense of the word could be reconstructed but also fossil Man.

I was always being asked, 'Is it possible to reconstruct a skull from the face? That is to say proceed vice versa?' To this question I can reply only that such an experiment would be absurd, for even if I succeeded in depicting the skull of my questioner that could not prove that I had killed the individual. But, joking apart, it is indeed impossible to reconstruct the skull from the face because it presents a very complicated shape and in the facial part possesses innumerable very delicate features. The face, on the other hand, is a simplified version of the complicated skull shape. . . . A mathematician might formulate this in the following way: the skull provides more information than the face, therefore an adequate problem cannot be solved. A skull, it is true, allows of the face being reconstructed but not a skull from a face, for in this case only an approximate diagram without details could be produced. But this diagram would all the same be an individual one and therefore fairly close to the real skull.

Usually it is thought that all skulls are more or less alike. But this is not so. Absolutely similar skulls do not exist and cannot exist. If the shape of two skulls is very similar, the one will be distinguished from the other by size and a complete resemblance in both size and shape is quite unthinkable. In this connection, however, we may ask ourselves, is it possible to imagine at least approximately what would be the face of a skull whose reconstruction one is undertaking? Of course this can be done but the possibility of such a mental vision comes only with experience.

For many years, I was in contact with Wulf Ginsburg in connection with my work. He is a physician, anatomist and anthrop-logist and at present a doctor of physiognomical science—all at once. When I first made his acquaintance (it was more than thirty years ago) he was studying at the Military Medical Academy. I owe him much since he made possible the beginning of my work especially by placing at my disposal X-ray photographs of the heads of living men from which I reconstructed profiles. Then I compared my model with the radiograph, which was taken with weak rays and so allowed the soft parts to be clearly seen. Once he gave me a series of pictures which at a first glance I recognised as those of Wulf himself. At once I said to him, 'When did you have yourself radiographed?' He was astounded, for he had wanted to play a trick on me. Often later on my pupils would present me with similar 'cases', but to their disappointment, I was always up to their dodges. Not so long ago Galina Lebedinskaya slipped in among a collection a radiograph of herself. I was rather annoyed with her and said, 'Listen, Galina, here's another picture with hair-pins, you shouldn't be radiographed so often.'

And now my pupils also have acquired the capacity to guess at the facial traits from a skull.

A Large-scale Test

A series of successful experiments in reconstructing the faces of recent Man encouraged me to undertake the fulfilment of a long cherished wish . . . that is to say to create authentic portraits of fossil Man. What led up to these experiments was a discovery of some remains of prehistoric Man which had just been made.

S. N. Bibikov, the archaeologist, had found in the Mursak-Koba cave (Crimea) a double grave dated to the late Upper Palaeolithic—the so-called Azilian-Tardenoisian phase. In the grave were the remains of an elderly man and a young woman. The skeletons were, considering their age, quite well preserved. From the female skull I reconstructed the portrait of a young, good-looking woman of classical Cro-Magnon type. Various experts approved of this work and a little later I got a very important letter in which I was asked whether I was the same

Mikhail Gerasimov who had in 1924–5 at the medical high school at Irkutsk begun working on the problem of portrait reconstruction. If I was the same person, then a large-scale test-experiment could be arranged. The letter was signed A. D. Grigoriev.

Professor Grigoriev, my old teacher at Irkutsk, was by now holding the chair of Forensic Medicine at the 3rd Medical University College in Moscow. He had at his disposal the largest Moscow mortuary in Lefortovo. A few days later I was in Moscow, met Grigoriev and discussed with him how the test-experiment should be conducted. He already knew something of what I had been doing lately and judged it very favourably and added that if a large-scale experiment was successful then my method might be used even in criminological work.

The programme we arranged together was as follows: the chosen heads would be photographed in profile and full-face, the photographs numbered and the skulls after having had the flesh removed were to receive the same numbers. The photographs were enclosed in sealed envelopes and placed in the mortuary safe. The skulls were to be sent to me in Leningrad. Professor Grigoriev himself took no part in choosing the skulls and I had no contact with the mortuary staff that had prepared them. Everything was so arranged that neither Professor Grigoriev nor I knew anything about the skulls I received; they simply bore a registered number.

After my reconstructions had been completed I presented the heads at three separate meetings arranged by the faculties of forensic medicine and normal anatomy of the 3rd Medical College together with the department of anthropology at Moscow University. The meetings were attended by criminologists and examining magistrates. At the first meeting I presented six heads—of three Russian men, one Russian woman, one Pole and a Chinese. . . . A month later at a second meeting I showed four further skulls, all of men, a Russian and three Ukrainians. And again a month later came the third meeting at which only two heads were presented—one of a man of Baltic origin and the other clearly of a Caucasian.

The results exceeded even my expectations. All the reconstructions proved to be like portraits although they were of persons of both sexes, of various ages and of different racial affinities. All the twelve heads were so true to life that their identity with the relevant photographs was undoubted. The reconstructions differed only from the photographs in one thing: I had been careful to reproduce the features of a living individual whereas the photographs were all of corpses which had been subjected to post-mortem examinations.

In connection with these experiments I had the following amusing experience. I have already mentioned I was living in Leningrad; the heads, however, were presented in Moscow. I took with me for the first meeting two cases. They contained three of the modelled heads. According to the railways regulations then in force such cases could not be taken as hand-luggage. It seemed to me that it would be very risky to register the cases, since the heads were of wax and might easily get damaged. Therefore I had asked the director of the Institute to give me a certificate. This was duly made out; the secretary handed it to me and I stuffed it, unread, into my pocket. As I had foreseen the conductor would not let me take my cases on to the train, so I held out the certificate to him. At once he went pale, his lips began to tremble and he almost threw the paper back in my face. With some difficulty he managed to explain that on no account would he allow me with such luggage into the compartment. Such horror was shown on his face that I began to fear that something was not in order. The certificate read:

> 'Comrade Gerasimov is travelling on official business in order to make a report to the chair of forensic medicine at the 3rd Medical University College in Moscow. He is taking with him two cases which contain human heads. It is requested . . .'

I looked at the conductor and said, 'But they're only wax heads . . .' No, he would not discuss the matter any more, so I ran off to the station-master and explained things to him, told him who I was, where I wanted to go and what sort of heads I had in my luggage. He solved the problem but insisted I should open one of the cases. This I did and showed him the reconstructions. The permission was granted, but in some way or another the rumour had got about throughout the carriage that I was carrying human heads with me, that they came from dead men but looked like the heads of living persons. It was not two minutes before my compartment was completely emptied. No one wanted to sit near me and travel with my horrible luggage.

But now let us get back to my test experiments. A. D. Grigoriev, who had organised and presided over the meetings at which he had taken careful notes of the speeches, after the discussion gave a summary which was recorded and confirmed by all present. Professor Grigoriev, indeed, attributed a great significance to my experiments and considered it possible that my methods might be utilised in criminological practice. In any case the large-scale test reconstructions had been successful. The problem of portrait reconstructions from skulls was solved.

More than twenty years passed. Much had been modified in my work. A whole series of publications on the problem had appeared. I submitted my paper on 'The foundations for facial reconstruction from skulls' for the academic grade of 'Candidate in Biological Sciences'. Later the paper was published as a book with the same title.

Innumerable reconstructions of recent and fossil Man have since been made and our method has been extensively utilised in criminal cases. In the Ethnographical Institute of the U.S.S.R. Academy of Sciences a laboratory for plastic reconstruction has been established. There my pupils work and there we have together discovered much that is new. They have adopted for themselves the principles of my method and use them, both in preliminary investigations of criminal cases and in anthropological work for the creation of remarkable portraits of men who lived long ago. Although the foundations of my reconstruction method have remained unchanged, my pupils have been able to verify and to refine many of my observations. I myself was awarded the degree of doctor of facial science.

Help in Clearing Up Crimes

The problem of portrait-reconstruction was thus solved empirically. Many dozens of reconstructions of faces from skulls of unknown persons had proved the correctness of the method employed. In all cases the copies presented an individual portrait likeness which could be checked by comparison with photographs of the person concerned.

Empirical experiment furnished the foundation for the methodical determination of certain constant proceedings for reconstruction. After long years spent in collecting and checking factual material, I was able to provide standard measurements for soft parts, account being taken of individual variations in skulls. So was built up little by little a scientific method of reconstruction.

We had promised ourselves that the method would be of no little assistance in preliminary investigations of criminal cases. But like everything else new our method came up against much reticence and even prejudice among criminologists. An undoubted and very considerable objection to the employment of our method was, in its earlier phases, that I alone was master of the method. Its objectivity was questioned, it was held even that it was unscientific, and that I happened to possess an unusual, individual, gift of guessing right. It would be most risky to make use of my method in criminal law cases.

But all the same my method was proved to be necessary. Fairly often the victims of murder could not be identified during preliminary investigations, and this was true most of all in cases where the bodies had lain in circumstances which hastened the process of decomposition. Corpses of persons drowned or burned, moreover, afforded no clues to identity at all. Often corpses are purposely mutilated so as to make them unrecognisable. But in such cases it is possible to reconstruct the face from the skull—or even from fragments of the skull if they have been preserved—and thus lead to the identification of the victim.

More than twenty-five years had passed since the first experiments in the reconstruction of faces from skulls had taken place in connection with criminal cases and now my method was gaining slowly, very slowly, its *raison d'être*.

In the years that have gone by I have alone undertaken about 100 reconstructions of faces from skulls for identification purposes. In more recent years my pupils G. V. Lebedinskaya, T. S. Surnina, V. P. Petrov and Heinrich Ullrich have prepared more than forty reconstructions at the request of the judicial authorities.

Practically no case is known in our laboratory where an individual could not be identified.

However, in the earliest days the most noted criminologists had violently opposed the introduction of my method, which must seem all the more astonishing since in the course of our reconstruction process we could determine the sex and biological age of an unknown person and ascertain individual peculiarities such as lameness. In connection with the portrait there is constituted a very important complex of indications serving for reliable identification of a victim.

It is not possible here to deal with this theme at length, and we hope that the reader will be satisfied with the examples from criminal cases. These will, we think, indicate the significance of the method.

We carried out those described below at the request of the investigating officials. Our task consisted mainly in creating a portrait reconstruction from a skull of an unknown person. The research institute of the militia then compared our reconstructed heads with photographs of missing persons. Declarations of acquaintances and relations would be taken and possibly in addition so called 'applications' might be undertaken in the laboratory, that is the superposition of photographs of living persons on the reconstruction and skull.

Identification of a Boy

This case is of especial interest since it was the first of its sort in our annals of crime and moreover very noteworthy for the technique of identification.

It happened in Leningrad in 1939. A young and still inexperienced examining magistrate was assigned to a very difficult case. The only evidence he had to go on was the bones of an unknown person. There was nothing more. He must, however, tackle the job. But he did not know where to begin.

The facts were these: in a wood not far from Leningrad, but distant from any settlement, the scattered bones of a human skeleton were discovered quite by chance. They lay spread over an area of about 12 by 15 metres. The epiphyses of several of the bones including some of the vertebrae showed clear traces of some carnivores' teeth. Therefore it was thought probable that the person in question had been torn to pieces by wolves. But after a thorough search of the site of the tragedy there were discovered, about 20 metres farther off, the skull and lower jaw of the victim.

The skull showed a number of traces of cuts which must have been made by a fine, very sharp blade. Judging from the state of the bones one would conclude that the individual must have died from five to seven months before their discovery. Clearly he had been still young, but more accurate information about the age, or indeed even the sex, of the victim was not forthcoming at the juridical investigation. As there was no object of any sort with the bones, the identification of the individual and the cause of his death remained undetermined.

As I entered the room of the examining magistrate he was working on a rough copy of his report on the case and the closure of the proceedings. He looked at me in an unfriendly way and said, 'What do you want?'

'Lieutenant Gudov of Section One of the militia administration has just told me that I should find the skeleton of an unknown man here.'

'Yes, and so what?'

'I've been working for more than fifteen years on the problems of portrait reconstruction and I think I can help you to identify these bones.'

'Madness, no one can help in this case,' he growled, 'but since you're here, pack up the bones. Anyway, one can say we've nothing to lose. In twelve hours I must turn in the proof for the order closing the case. So it's all the same whether the bones go into the crematorium or are handed over to you.'

Half an hour later I was at my work-table. I spread out a large sheet of paper and then spread the bones carefully on it. The skeleton was not complete. The long bones were missing and of the vertebrae only a few remained. The skull was in good condition but covered with earth and grass. As I was beginning to clean it meticulously with a small brush, I noticed a good many small hairs on the paper. They were reddish blond and short. When the skull was cleaned there was revealed on the left side of the forehead the trace of a blow delivered by a blunt-edged weapon. On the right side of the head just above the mastoid process I could make out marks of numerous cuts obviously made with a light, small, hunting hatchet. This was no doubt a case of murder—and the blow on the forehead might well have been dealt with the back of the chopper. My task was simply to find out as nearly as possible the age and sex of the victim and then to model the face from the skull.

The incomplete bone formation, the quite open autures on the skull vault, the slight degree of wear of the teeth and the absence of wisdom teeth, all suggested that the individual was aged at the most twelve or thirteen years. It was a good deal more difficult to determine the sex since the victim was so young that the characteristic sex indications on the skull were only slightly marked. However, the rather strongly developed supraorbital region and also the area of the back of the head, the quite large mastoid processes, the relatively massive lower jaw and also the strong micro-relief of the whole facial skeleton, all pointed to its being the skull of a boy rather than of a girl. This conclusion was, in a measure, confirmed by the relatively massive structure of the bones of the extremities.

So about two hours later I had some evidence about the outward appearance of the victim. I at once telephoned the examining magistrate.

'Search among the missing persons, for a boy about twelve to thirteen years of age, short but strongly built, thick-set, with rather a long head and projecting back to the head, light reddish hair cut short with clippers—it must have been clipped about a week before the murder.'

The amazed answer came back:

'Why a lad? Why reddish blond?'

'I guarantee the truth of all I've told you. I'll give you my reasons later on.'

What I did not add on the telephone was that if he had been a little more observant he himself would have discovered the hairs and would have been able to deduce that the dead person had had reddish-blond hair clipped close.

The reproduction of the boy's skull needed special attention. Luckily I already possessed suitable material. Among the collection of X-ray photographs were more than a dozen of boys aged from nine to thirteen. So I could construct a diagram of the soft parts from the profile. It was only then that the real reconstruction could begin. It was an exacting task and demanded both the closest attention and much dexterity. Then the teeth and the lower jaw must be rightly put in place, and this, in the present instance, was no easy task since so many teeth were missing. Then the most important masticatory muscles were modelled in wax—they determine the whole shape of the face. Glass eyes were then fixed in wax. Little by little I reconstructed the lad's head taking into account the information available about the thickness of the soft parts in children of this age, and the individual peculiarities in the relief of the skull, together with the nasal bones, the dentition and the chin eminence. The boy was snub-nosed and chubby-cheeked, had a high forehead and a thick upper lip together with slightly projecting ears.

The following day at eleven o'clock I appeared before the examining magistrate and went with him to see the chief of Section One of the militia administration, Lieutenant Gudov. It had to be decided in what way the identification should be effected. A report of this sort had never before been drawn up. There was no precedent. One thing only was quite clear. The reconstructed head could not simply be presented to the boy's relations. If the wax head were shown to father or mother (especially if they do not know their son has died) they would be much alarmed and an objective identification would hardly be possible. On Gudov's suggestion we decided that at the interrogation the reconstruction itself should not be shown, but only a photograph of it mixed with many other photographs. So that the photograph of the reconstruction should differ as little as possible from those of living persons we took pictures of it with and without a cap, and with an overcoat. Finally we had seven photographs from various angles and in various positions. It needed very careful examination to see that it was not the picture of a living face.

Five days later the unknown victim was identified in my presence.

The examining magistrate had in the meanwhile ascertained that about six months earlier in the village of K., not far from where the bones of the unknown victim were found, a boy had disappeared. He had already left home several times before. Therefore his parents had not worried much about him . . . he was sure to turn up again and where could he disappear to? The relations believed that the adventurous lad would just wander about. The father of the boy was transferred by the examining magistrate to Leningrad where he was to be heard as a witness. During his examination he stated that his son was twelve, red-haired like his mother, bright, good at his lessons, liked reading but he did not care for working on the land and was always threatening to go off to the city. The father was sure his son was still alive. After his examination, he was shown as had been agreed more than thirty photographs of boys aged from twelve to thirteen, and among these was the reconstructed head of the dead boy. Without any hesitation the man picked out the pictures of the reconstructed head. It never struck him that they were anything other than photographs of the boy's real face. As he examined the pictures he murmured, 'Oh, what a fine coat he's got on, and his cap's new too. Things can't be going so badly with him.'

So the murdered boy was quite definitely identified. The first attempt to use a skull reconstruction in a criminal case was thus brilliantly successful.

The examining magistrate's further work went on without my collaboration. I only remember that in 1941 the case could be closed.

Valentina Kosova

On 24th April 1940 there disappeared from the town of V. a young woman by the name of Valentina Kosova. She was a girl of a cheerful disposition, communicative, a good comrade and a member of the Communist Youth Association. She was just twenty-two years old and was eight months pregnant. Practically on the eve of her pregnancy leave she suddenly disappeared. Her husband, A. Boiarintsev, against whom criminal proceedings were begun, was able to produce an alibi and was soon released owing to lack of evidence against him.

However, in August of the same year there were found not far from the town the skeletal remains of a pregnant woman. Naturally enough it was thought they might be those of the missing Valentina. Boiarintsev was again arrested but again set at liberty. It could not be proved that the skeleton was that of Valentina Kosova.

As the bones could not be identified they were buried and proceedings in the Valentina Kosova case had to be dropped for lack of evidence.

But about six months later the examining magistrate Kirkina came to V. on a tour of inspection and among the documents she examined were those relating to Valentina Kosova. As the case interested her, she examined closely what evidence had been produced, including the account of the discovery of the skeleton, and she came to the conclusion that the proceedings in the case had been unjustifiably dropped. After the remains of the unknown woman found in the woods had been exhumed Kirkina decided that the proceedings should be resumed.

Obviously the first thing to be done was to prove that the skeleton was really that of Valentina Kosova. The examining magistrate was aware of my work in reconstructing faces from skulls so she wrote to me asking if I would make a report on the skull and then sent it to me by post. On 3rd April 1941 I got the parcel.

The reader may remember that shortly before I had carried out a large-scale test experiment with skulls that had been sent to me on Professor Grigoriev's instructions from Moscow. For reasons of prudence and to be on the safe side I never opened postal parcels myself; that was done by my collaborators who, in every case, drew up a report on the matter. Only after this formality did I take over any given skull for treatment. For the opening of the parcel from the town of V. the usual little committee was appointed from among my colleagues and scientific assistants at the Institute for the History of Material Culture. B. B. Piotrovski headed the committee and the members were S. S. Chernikov and A. P. Kruglov. The parcel was opened and the skull given to me to work on. At the bottom of the box was a sealed envelope with an inscription stating that it contained a photograph of Valentina Kosova. The envelope was placed, unopened, in the Institute's safe.

Unfortunately the lower jaw was missing so that my work was made more difficult than it might have been—especially the reconstruction of the shape of chin and mouth and the lower part of the face. The skull was in good condition, only the two centre incisors were missing, while the second right-hand incisor had a gold crown. It was quite clear that the cranium was that of a woman. This was indicated by the size, the general conformation, the slight development of relief and the smallness of the mastoid processes. To judge by the open sutures and the not fully developed base of the skull, the slight amount of wear of the teeth and the juvenile character of the facial bones, the age of the individual could be set at between twenty and twenty-three years. The skull was high, rounded, the face of middling length, rather broad and somewhat flat but of regular, oval form with a slightly accentuated profile. The forehead was high with well-marked relief. The eye-orbits were not large but high, rectangular and with clearly defined lateral margins. The eyes had obviously been small with thick upper lids; the low eyebrows were almost straight, the nasal bones broad, not long and only slightly projecting, the nasal aperture not long . . . the nose itself must have been small, blunt, quite broad and rather tip-tilted. The dental arch was moderately broad so the mouth must have been small, regularly formed, full and with labial cleft.

The missing lower jaw was replaced by one from another skull which was chosen with due regard to the general breadth of the trochlea, the shape of the dentition, the mass and form of the lower jaw. All the same the reconstruction of the chin region proved to be difficult, but a more suitable lower jaw was not forthcoming although we ransacked the anthropological collections of the Ethnographical Museum of the U.S.S.R. Academy of Sciences and examined more than 350 jaws.

The real breadth of the face and the degree of prominence of the chin were not quite clear. As always in the reconstruction of a head the masticatory muscles were the first to be reconstituted. After that glass eyes were put in place, the profile curves built up and so forth. Each main phase of the reconstruction was photographed, and then the whole head, when the work was finished.

After that the members of the committee took the envelope out of the strong room. Now for the first time I saw a portrait of the living person. The photograph showed the face of a young girl, at the most sixteen or seventeen years of age. But Valentina had perished when she was twenty-two, thus some five or six years after the date of the photograph. Despite the considerable difference in age between the reconstruction and the portrait there was no doubt that it was the same face in both cases. The form of the face and the profile were very much alike in both representations while nose, forehead, eyebrows, eyes, cheeks and even the outline of the mouth were identical.

The reconstituted face conveyed a more adult and therefore a coarser impression, and that was natural not only on account of the difference in age but also because of Kosova's condition at the time of her death. She was expecting a child so the whole expression of her face must be influenced, at least to the extent that it no longer displayed the virginal freshness and softness shown in the photograph.

In fact, the likeness between the reconstruction and the portrait was so great that one could be practically certain that the skull really was that of Valentina Kosova. The correspondence between the biological age indicated by the bones and the 'calendrical' age of the missing woman would seem to exclude any possibility of error. Then there was the statement of eyewitnesses that Valentina had had a gold tooth on a second incisor—and the corresponding tooth of the skull also had a gold crown.

So all the material evidence justified the conclusion that the skull actually was that of the missing Valentina Kosova.

At the request of the examining magistrate Kirkina photographs of the reconstituted head and my reports were sent to the public prosecutor's office in the town of V.

Boiarintsev was tried, found guilty and confessed to the murder.

Later on Kirkina, the examining magistrate, told me that during the preparations for the trial several photographs had been found of Kosova taken shortly before her death. These portraits showed an even stronger resemblance to the reconstructed face than had the photograph sent to me.

Alexander B.

During the severe fighting around Moscow a young officer was killed, one Alexander B. When the war was over his parents obtained permission to have their son's remains exhumed. It was known where he was buried, but matters were complicated by the fact that two bodies had been interred in the same grave. Alexander B.'s bones were identified from descriptions of the wounds he had suffered and also by the metal tab that was attached to the remains. The relations as a whole were convinced that these were the right ones, but Alexander's mother was assailed by doubt. So the parents sought me out and asked me to help them. This was a request that obviously I could not refuse.

It was towards the end of 1946 when the skull was handed over to me. It came from a man who was at the most twenty to twenty-two years old at the time of his death—and this corresponded to the actual age of Alexander B. The relief of the skull indicated that he must have been a strong man, mature for his age.

We can omit a detailed description of the reconstruction work since in all cases the same technique is used in the same succession, but I should like to refer here to a few peculiarities in this case. The position of the eyebrows was determined by the margins of the eye-sockets. The formation of the nose-forehead area and the relief of the supraorbital region defined the actual trace of the eyebrows' lines. While I was reconstructing the eyes and the forehead my attention was drawn to the unusual form of the median part of the eye-sockets. As I modelled the lines of the eyebrows, the relief of the supraorbital region was so peculiar that the whole expression of the face conveyed an impression of care and tension hardly to be expected in one so young. The nose was moderately prominent, quite broad and slightly undulating when seen in profile. The skull appeared prognathous, the arches of the jaw were broad, the teeth rather large and they met in a characteristic 'scissors bite' whereby the incisors of the upper jaw largely covered the base of the lower jaw. The mouth was comparatively wide and the lips were thick. The face would have appeared quite youthful had not the lips been so tightly compressed. The chin was strong.

The work went on slowly. Several times I was so dissatisfied with what I had produced that I destroyed what I had done and had to begin all over again. Finally the head was ready.

But now it had to be shown to the parents. No one knows a son's appearance better than his mother. She knows all her children's peculiarities down to the smallest hidden feature. In this case I was not sure that the head really was that of Alexander B. In these circumstances I wanted to show the reconstruction first of all to another member of the family and to inform the parents only when I was quite sure where I stood. So I asked the man's sister to come and see me.

She appeared at the appointed time. She was a year younger than her brother and might have been twenty-two or twenty-three years old. She was a student. In my laboratory one whole wall was covered with shelves on which were maybe a hundred heads. There were portraits of historical personages, of fossil men and of contemporaries. The reconstruction of Alexander's head I had purposely put down on a shelf near the floor where it was not noticeable. To the right and left of Alexander's head were those of young individuals which did not differ from each other at all essentially. When the sister came into the room she stopped. Her eyes ranged over the shelves. Then she said slowly: 'Oh, how many there are, and these here, these horrible ones, they are of primitive Man, I suppose?' Then immediately afterwards she asked in quite other accents, 'Mikhail Mikhailovich, didn't Alexander have thicker lips?' for she had quickly recognised her brother's head. I answered, 'No, you were not accustomed to looking at him from above because he was considerably taller than you.' Then I put the head on the table and the sister sat down opposite and examined the reconstruction very carefully for a long time during which she turned the head this way and that examining it from the side and also from behind. She stared at it in silence as though she were spellbound. Then she took a deep breath and whispered, 'Yes, of course, it's Alexander, the head is very like his. I think I can show it to Mother.'

The following day the mother came. I was very excited. Colleagues from the Anthropological Museum of Moscow University were also present.

The head stood on a table in the middle of the room. My colleagues stood apart near the window so as not to be obtrusive. While she was still in the anteroom the mother asked where the portrait was. Her movements were hasty and nervous, but she was still quite a young-looking woman. When she entered the room she turned very pale and stumbled. I was just in time to give her a chair. She sat silently for a long time then dissolved in tears. She seemed to be aware of nothing around her but the head of her son. The silence became oppressive. I cannot say how long it was before she managed to murmur: 'Thank you, that is he.' She took a handkerchief from her bag and wiped away her tears, then with a sad smile on her face she fumbled about in the bag and handed me a small photograph. It was of Alexander when still quite young. The face had something completely boyish about it, a calm, naive look, a full, irresolute mouth, childish cheeks and a rounded chin. The resemblance to the reconstruction was unmistakable. Nevertheless, 'my' Alexander displayed manly features and no longer had anything childish in his face. The reconstructed visage had a tense expression and betokened a strong will. I said, 'Yes, I no longer doubt that this is your son. But it seems to me that the portrait is not quite successful. Shall I correct something? Change the facial expression? Make it rather softer perhaps?'

The mother once more examined the portrait of her son:

'No, it is very like him, he looks just as he did a week before his death when he said good-bye to us . . .'

Half an hour later she took leave of us, but ten days later all three, the father, the mother and the sister, came to fetch Alexander's bust that I had moulded in plaster.

The Search for N.S.

At the beginning of 1948 a thirty-two-year-old woman disappeared from a small town in the southern Ukraine. One morning she left her house, and did not return that evening, the next day or a week later. There seemed to be no reason for her sudden disappearance. A search was made for her at the homes of relations and friends. An official warrant was issued. But still no trace of her.

About eight months passed, then in an old wartime trench the remains of an unknown woman were found. On examination of the skeleton the cause of death was shown to be murder. As no other woman than N.S. had been reported missing in the neighbourhood, there was a strong suspicion that the remains were hers. It was decided that for verification the face was to be reconstructed from the skull found.

So in February 1950 the skull of the unknown individual was sent to me. As the examining magistrate knew that it is impossible to guess just what any particular hair-style may have been, he sent me with the skull a photographic copy of N.S.'s coiffure. The first thing that struck me about the skull was that a considerable portion had been broken away. The left temporal bone, the lower part of the occipital and the base of the skull were missing. I could not imagine with what implement such severe damage could be inflicted. So at I once informed the examining magistrate that the injuries must have been caused by a shell splinter and the woman must have been killed during the war.

But the examining magistrate did not agree with me. He was quite convinced that the remains belonged to the woman N.S. reported missing in 1948. The state of the sutures suggested that the skull belonged to a young woman aged from twenty-six to twenty-eight. To determine the age more precisely was difficult, since most of the teeth had been lost after death. The first and second molars which remained were relatively little worn down and the third molar had not yet erupted. In a month my work was done and I presented my reconstruction for identification to the public prosecutor's office.

The examining magistrate compared the reconstruction with the photograph of N.S. It needed only a cursory glance to see that the reconstruction and the photograph did not correspond at all—either in general appearance or in details. The skull and the reconstructed head were of elongated proportions, the skull vault was relatively low, the forehead was narrow and high with strongly marked supraorbital region and rather high eyebrows.

The face was narrow and long and the profile accentuated.

On the other hand, the N.S. photographs showed quite different features. The skull vault was wide, rounded and high, the forehead broad with only slightly developed supraorbital regions and the eyebrows low. The face was of shortened proportions, wide, flat and considerably older than the copy.

Such a gross divergence between the reconstruction and the photograph of the living person could not be the result of an error on my part. I might have been mistaken regarding this or that detail of the face such as the tip of the nose or the lips incorrectly modelled, but I could not have misrepresented the main correlations of the whole head. The skull would not have allowed this. The lack of resemblance was so striking that all those present doubted whether the skull presented for identification really was that of the missing N.S.

But in order to track down a possible fault either in the reconstruction or in the preliminary inquiry I built up the reconstruction again and I compared the bare skull with the photograph of N.S. A thorough investigation during the destruction of the wax model brought to light no important mistake. Even if I had to start all over again and create another reconstruction I would produce what to all intents and purposes would be the same visage and there was no reason to think the reconstruction incorrect. The modelled head conformed with the morphology of the skull in all important respects. When it was free from its wax the skull was photographed in exactly the same format and from the same angle as the face in picture of N.S.

From a technical point of view this presented no great difficulty. But, all the same, the anatomy of the face must be known, since on the superposition of the reconstituted head and the photograph of a living person certain quite definite morphological points must coincide exactly. From the photograph of the face a negative was prepared.

In the case in question skull and face did not correspond. The answer then to the problem as to whether the skull came from the missing N.S. must be NO.

Preliminary investigations were resumed, but now two women instead of one were being sought—N.S., missing since the beginning of 1948 and aged thirty-two, and then the unknown woman whose skeleton was found at the end of 1948. Then it was remembered that with the latter a gold watch, a chain and an emerald ear-ring had also been unearthed. On being questioned, N.S.'s relations said they had never seen such valuables in her possession.

About six months later the examining magistrate P., who was working on the case, informed me that the women whose head I had reconstructed from the skull had been recognised and identified by relations and many friends after they had seen the reconstruction. This woman had disappeared a long time before, right at the beginning of the war. Relations also described in detail the jewellery and recognised it when it was shown to them.

But the missing N.S. remained missing and up to now no trace of her has ever been found. Maybe she is still alive.

The Skeleton in Gavanskaya Street

The war was at an end. A young lieutenant who had been wounded returned to his home in Leningrad. But his home was occupied by strangers. All his relations had perished in the siege. So he rented a small room in Gavanskaya Street. On visiting his new lodging he was struck by a very ugly, reddish-brown, greasy-looking stain on the ceiling. The room was on the top floor of a large house and was directly under the attic. So the young officer climbed up into the loft, found the space over his room and the corner where the stain was. Behind the wooden rafters he came upon a mattress of striped ticking mottled with dark-brown blotches. He tugged at the mattress and the rotted stuff ripped open and there came to light bones, undoubtedly human. He thought the remains were those of a man killed during the war and he asked the house superintendent to have the body at once removed.

The latter alerted the militia. Shortly afterwards a representative of the criminal police accompanied by a forensic medicine expert came on the scene. In the loft and in the mattress was the half-mummified body of a human being. The self-sufficient young expert did not take the trouble to examine the remains carefully but after a rapid and superficial examination made his report 'mummified corpse of a man. Age 25–35. Dismembered with an axe.' So began the inquiry into the case of the unknown man in Gavanskaya Street.

A year later the laboratory for plastic reconstruction in the Ethnographical Institute of the U.S.S.R. Academy of Sciences received instructions to prepare a facial reconstruction of a skull which appeared to be that of a male aged between twenty-five and thirty-five.

It happened that at the time I was very ill, so my colleague Taisiya Surnina had to undertake this difficult task. It was only her second independent piece of work. On the fifth day she came in great perplexity to see me. From this supposedly male skull a female face emerged. I told her to remove the wax and start all over again. But there was disappointment again. The reconstruction presented a woman's face. I advised Taisiya Surnina to model only one half of the face and then to show me how it looked. A week later a modelled half-head was brought to me. It was decidedly massive but it showed the beautiful face of a woman. I examined the two halves carefully, the reconstruction and the bare half of the skull. It was undoubtedly feminine. 'Why do you want to model the head of a man? Can't you see the skull is that of a woman?'—'Yes, but in the instructions we got, it says "male head" . . . As the body was mummified a mistake is unlikely.'

I examined the skull once more and said: 'Don't worry about the instructions but go ahead and finish the job. I can't see any mistake you've made and I think you are right. But there must be a mistake somewhere. Our task is to be objective and to model the face from the skull. If the skull is of a female, then the face also must be that of a woman.'

A fortnight later the head was ready. Taisiya Surnina photographed it herself and sent it to Leningrad. A week later I got a furious letter from the examining magistrate who wrote that if we did not understand anything about reconstruction then we should not meddle with it and try to mislead examining magistrates.

Six months later I attended a criminologists' congress in Leningrad and gave a talk on the method of facial reconstruction from skulls and its practical use in preliminary criminal investigations. Thereupon I described the case of the reconstruction of a female face from a supposed male skull found in Gavanskaya Street. I showed those present the letter from the examining magistrate and I energetically defended Taisiya Surnina's work. In the course of the discussion I learned that the examining magistrate had destroyed the reconstruction . . . but he had not found his man and the case was dropped. But I insisted on its being reopened. In the lieutenant's room there had lodged before him a certain Fetisova, a young woman aged twenty-two. She disappeared a year before the young officer arrived. As she had left almost nothing behind her in her room, the impression was that she was travelling.

During a conversation that was to help clear up certain points the examining magistrate showed me quite unexpectedly a photograph of the missing Fetisova and at once I remembered the head modelled by Taisiya Surnina. I was quite sure, just from memory, that the photograph and the reconstituted head represented one and the same woman.

As I had now seen the photograph naturally I could not objectively execute a reconstitution. Therefore I proposed a superposition to the examining magistrate. The result was as expected. The photograph of Fetisova agreed with the skull found above her room in Gavanskaya Street.

Shortly afterwards the criminal was discovered. The case was reported in the newspapers. The trial was held in public and I was present as an expert. The criminal confessed and was found guilty of murder.

The Identification of M.

In 1950 I was commissioned to reconstruct the face of an elderly woman whose skeleton had been found inside a hut out in the middle of the woods. About a year earlier the wife of a forester had disappeared in strange circumstances. She had wanted to go and visit her son at the neighbouring town but she neither turned up at her son's home nor did she return to her own. All search was fruitless.

There were some indications that suggested the skeleton found in the hut might be that of the forester's missing wife. The skull had no lower jaw. All the teeth except three molars on the right side had been lost and only the roots of the incisors remained in place. A large portion of the alveolar arch of the upper jaw had been lost. The surface of the occipital bones showed many round holes and in the base of the skull there was lodged a large shot. One got the impression the woman had been killed by a shot-gun which must have been discharged against the lower part of the face.

Before I began on reconstructing the face I built up the missing teeth and the lower jaw. I was told that the forester's wife wore her hair parted on the right side, brushed down flat and caught up at the back into a small, tightly twisted bun.

When the head was finished it was presented for identification. In 1950 the commission of third instance with the chief medical expert of the U.S.S.R. Ministry of Public Health confirmed the undoubted resemblance between the reconstructed head and a photograph affixed to a certificate issued on 6th October 1946, at her dwelling-place, to a certain M. born in 1900. So the forester's wife was identified.

The following is the declaration made by the forester: 'My wife wanted to go and see our son so I drove her off towards the station. On the way she began to find fault with me. I was quite rightly angry, so I said to her, "Drive on alone and leave the horse and waggon with the pointsman at the station.' 'Then I jumped off the waggon pulling my double-barrelled shotgun towards me. Then suddenly two shots rang out. The horse was frightened and bolted. Shortly afterwards the reins got caught in the wheels and the waggon came to a stop. I ran after it. My wife was dead. One shot had torn away all the lower part of her face and the second shot had lodged in her chest. I was very frightened and instead of taking the body to the station and reporting the accident to the militia, I drove off into the thick of the forest to an old deserted turf-hut where I buried the body. When the head of the militia questioned me about the disappearance of my wife, I did not confess my unintentional crime.'

The Identification of M.P.

On 21st April 1950 I received a communication from the Medico-legal Institute of the U.S.S.R. Ministry of Public Health. The letter read as follows:

> 'To the senior assistant in the Ethnographical Institute M. M. Gerasimov:
>
> The Medico-legal Institute of the U.S.S.R. Ministry of Public Health asks you to undertake a reconstruction of the face of an unknown person whose skull will be handed over to you by the forensic medicine expert Bogudskaya.
>
> per A. I. Polyanski
> *The Director of the Institute*'

A few days later I got the cleaned skull of the unknown person together with a note stating that the remains had been found in remarkable circumstances. The corpse had been discovered in a stack of straw and was naked. Some shreds of clothing were present. The remains were in such a condition that identification was impossible. Therefore a reconstruction of the skull was necessary.

According to the official record No. 114, the unknown person had collapsed from exhaustion and then frozen to death. The body showed no signs of violence.

From a thorough examination of the skull I judged that the age of the unknown person could be fixed at about twenty-four to twenty-five years. The reconstruction presented the head and face of a young man and was photographed from three angles. On 19th June 1950 the medico-legal affairs expert, Dadina, told me that the photographs of the reconstituted head had been reproduced in a number of copies and had been distributed with a view to identification of the unknown young man.

Three months later we got some more news. A certain Kh. living in the Voronezh area recognized in the photographs shown to her the portrait of her son Kh. M.P. born in 1925. She said that he worked in the Moscow district and lived in the village of D. but had not given news of himself for a long time. The manager of the business where the man worked declared to the examining magistrate that M.P. in the late autumn of the preceding year had suffered an attack of mental aberration, run away from his job and had not been seen again. The mother mentioned the name of the village near which M.P. had been found dead in a stack of straw.

So the unknown was identified, the cause of death was ascertained. The case was closed.

The Fate of Dr. Nina Z

In 1951 I had an attack of pneumonia. It was accompanied by a high fever and I felt dreadfully weak. On the evening of the 10th January there was a telephone call for me; it came from an examining magistrate by the name of Petrov who had just flown into Moscow from a great distance in order to get from me an expert opinion in a very complicated case. My mother told him I was ill, but in spite of this Petrov insisted on seeing me, so I agreed to meeting him and a little later a man of about forty-two years of age came into the room. When he saw me lying in bed he was quite embarrassed:

'Oh, I didn't believe it when your mother said you were ill—but you really are.'

I replied: 'Well, since you are here, sit down, sit down near me and fire away.'

This was his story.

In a town in the Urals lived a lady dentist, Nina Z., about thirty-two years old, with a little daughter of nine. She lived a very retired life, was separated from her husband, but no divorce had been pronounced. Nina made a very good living and did not depend on support from her husband. She had a sister living in the same town as herself.

Two years before, the husband, after a long silence, had given news of himself. In a letter he asked her to forgive him, not to bear a grudge but to come with their daughter and see him. Nina was touched, for she was really very fond of her husband and the separation had made her most unhappy. So after having given the matter much thought she decided to go to her husband at M. From there she wrote to her sister that things were going very well. Her husband had received her with open arms, was very attentive and more affectionate to herself and their daughter than he had ever been before. But finally Nina had to go back to her professional practice, as her two months' leave were up. But she decided that she would wind up her affairs and then return to live permanently with her husband. When the day came for her to leave him she sent a telegram to her sister in the Urals. Then the incredible happened.

Nina did indeed set out but she never reached home. The sister made inquiries of the husband. He was astonished that Nina had never got back. The railway police were alerted and a search made, but the dentist Nina Z. and her nine-year-old daughter could not be found.

The case was taken in hand by the examining magistrate Petrov. He set to work and systematically, step by step, traced Nina's route from the Urals to M. His thorough investigations led him to the conclusion that Nina had never left the town of M. A checking of the cloakroom receipt book confirmed his suspicions. On the day of Nina's supposed departure objects had been deposed in her husband's name and then three days later taken out. In addition Petrov learned by extensive inquiries that Nina and her daughter accompanied by the husband certainly did go to the station but had not returned home and since then had no longer been seen in the town. So it appeared that mother and daughter must be sought for within the limits of the town of M.

The search began. A distinguishing mark of Nina's was a gold crown on the first incisor on the left side. Petrov checked all the records of autopsies made on unknown persons in the town during the preceding two years. But there was no single reference to a woman with a gold tooth. The town had only one mortuary. Petrov questioned all the staff but no one could remember the body of a woman with a gold tooth—no, no one. Still, Petrov was sure that the trace of the missing Nina must be found in M. One day, late in the evening he chanced to sit on a bench next to an old watchman at the mortuary. They got into conversation. They smoked one cigarette after another. The old man told the story of his life. And then Petrov remarked casually that he knew an examining magistrate who was looking for a woman with a gold tooth. She had been missing for about two years. Thereupon the old man livened up, but, of course, the matter did not concern him, but he did say that a sister of his worked as a cleaner in the mortuary. . . . Petrov chatted for about another half-hour with the old man, and then, since it was becoming late, took his leave.

The next morning Petrov sent for the cleaner. She told him this story: about eighteen months before the body of a young woman, who had apparently drowned herself, had been brought into the mortuary. On examining the corpse the forensic medicine expert at once noticed the gold tooth. He carefully removed the crown and took it with a pincette to the window in order to see whether the crown was of real gold. His hand must have been trembling for the crown fell out of the window into the street. The whole staff went to hunt for it but it could not be found. Therefore in the postmortem report the crown was not mentioned.

So a woman at the most thirty-five years of age and with a gold tooth had been found drowned, but there was no proof that this body was that of the missing Nina.

After the opening of a series of graves Petrov with great difficulty found the skeleton of the drowned woman. An employee of the mortuary stated that with her a child also had been buried, so here was another clue for the identification of the skeleton. Petrov had come to Moscow with the skull and with the hope that I should be able to identify the missing Nina Z.

When he had finished his story he added: 'Since you are sick we must be patient.'

'And where is the skull?' I asked.

'In the anteroom.'

I asked my mother to put a drawing-board on my bed and to spread a sheet on it. Petrov brought me the skull.

It was undoubtedly that of a female and, judging from the state of the cranial sutures and the formation of the base of the skull, the woman could hardly have been more than thirty-five years old. Almost all the teeth were missing. In the upper jaw only one remained—the second molar, but in the lower jaw there were on the right the second molar and on the left the canine, the first premolar and the second molar. The degree of wear of these teeth indicated a somewhat younger age than thirty-five—perhaps from thirty to thirty-three. The margin of the right incisor socket was thickened so as to form a torus—a proof that this incisor had long been furnished with a metal crown. So the age and the trace of the crown seemed to strengthen Petrov's supposition that this really was the skull of Nina Z. While I was examining the cranium I heard something rustle. At first I thought it was a piece of desiccated brain tissue, but as I looked more carefully inside I saw it was a morsel of woven stuff. I drew it out carefully with a pair of pincers and promised Petrov I would preserve it.

The long visit had very much tired me and I asked the examining magistrate to come back in two days' time. I assured him that by then I would have done everything to make further investigation possible. The next day I sent the skull into the laboratory with a request for a drawing to be prepared of the skull both in profile and full face.

My mother and I then sponged and cleaned the piece of stuff. It was well preserved and 29×4 centimetres large. A clearly marked sewn hem indicated that it must have come from the collar of a blouse.

On examining the cleaned skull I was struck by a very significant peculiarity in its formation. On the right side the cheek-forehead suture seemed to be somewhat gaping. At first I thought this condition must have been due to a blow, but when I examined this fissure through a five-power magnifying-glass I saw that this was no trace of a blow but an atrophy of the bone during the lifetime of the subject. Further it could be seen that the whole right side of the skull displayed a certain weakness in its relief. This phenomenon I attributed to some disturbance in the functioning of the nerves of the face and neck. I thought it probable that the woman had suffered for a number of years from a paralysis of the facial nerves—a right-sided facial paresis. This must have been especially noticeable in the upper right eyelid. If the form of the left eyelid was normal then the right eyelid must have drooped considerably and indeed have covered part of the side of the eye.

At the appointed time Petrov appeared. I presented him with the result of my observations. He heard me with great interest but he remained outwardly calm though he told me afterwards that he could restrain himself only with difficulty.

In his briefcase was a photograph of Nina. He had got it from her sister. The portrait showed her as she was shortly before leaving to visit her husband—and she was wearing a blouse from which came the piece of stuff Petrov had beside him on the table. The photograph also showed that Nina's eyes did not match, that is to say they were of different shapes. The right eyelid drooped considerably. So here was enough to identify the lady dentist. But Petrov all the same must have a reconstruction since he hoped with its help to convict the criminal.

By 19th January I had finished a graphical reconstruction of the eyes and the profile of the head before proceeding to the plastic reconstitution and at the end of January the head was finished. Out of consideration for my state of health the experts came to my house. As usual, I had once again reproduced the hair from verbal descriptions and only after the head had been shown was I allowed to see the photograph.

The resemblance was obvious. The shape of the face, the mouth and the nose was very well reproduced. The eyes were almost identical in photograph and reproduction, the left normal and the right with drooping lid. Perfectly right also was the asymmetry of the eyes.

Petrov had a photograph prepared that purposely was not very clear—it looked rather like a bad amateur snapshot. This photograph of the reconstruction was laid before Nina's husband. He gazed with complete calm at the picture and admitted that it was indeed a portrait of his wife although not a very good one. The examining magistrate asked if he was quite sure. Again he answered, yes, thereupon Petrov asked him to write on the photograph that it was one of his wife.

An hour later he was charged with the murder of his wife and his daughter.

3 *The Essentials of the Method*

As everyone knows, our faces are always changing. They grow, they develop and then they begin to age. At the same time our skulls also change.

All individuals, independently of race, with a markedly developed glabells have in that region thicker soft parts than persons with a feebly developed supraorbital area. In the case of recent Man these soft parts vary in thickness from 8 to 12 millimetres (for males) and from 5 to 8 millimetres (in the case of females). The thickness of the soft parts at the root of the nose also does not vary according to racial type but depends directly on the degree of relief of area above the orbits and on the angle made by the projection of the nasal bones. Wide cheek-bones, flattened anteriorly, indicate a greater thickness of soft parts of the cheeks—and vice versa.

The greater the size of the jaw, the larger will be the masticatory muscles and the more developed the soft parts of the lower face.

What is called the 'biological' age of an individual hardly ever coincides with the 'calendrical' age. Therefore, to estimate the age of any individual the whole of the biological data must be taken into account. For instance, the obliteration (i.e. the fusing) of the skull sutures occurs generally after the age of about fifty-five or sixty but the obliteration may be delayed owing to endocrinal disturbances. In such cases we may estimate the real age from the degree of wear of the teeth—although damage or decay often distorts the evidence. However, experience has shown that if all the changes due to age are taken into account, the 'biological' age of an individual can be determined to within a margin of error of only two or three years.

Senile changes in the configuration of the skull are very revealing since they are accompanied by marked alterations in the face. Loss of teeth, for example, causes lasting modifications not only in the alveolar margins of the jaws but also leads to a reduction of the whole masticatory apparatus. The dental arch becomes flatter and thinner. The lower jaw especially changes its form and the chin region becomes more prominent. The habitual wearing of false teeth ('dentures') slows down, to a certain extent, the reduction of the jaw and helps to preserve the original shape of the mandible. Nevertheless, the gums become gradually flattened and the contour of the jaw itself becomes more slender and rounded.

With the reduction of the masticatory apparatus is associated a general displacement downwards of the upper part of the face. The shrinkage of the upper jaw modifies the shape of the nasal opening so that the typical senile drooping of the point of the nose is seen. Such changes in the facial skeleton induce modifications in the shape of the soft parts. The cheeks, for instance, in very old people are generally speaking thinner than are those of the young.

It is very important for portrait reconstruction that the poise of the head should be determined. A senile poise is caused not only by deformation of the backbone but also by the form of the condyles at the skull's base.

The 'sexing' of bones is not only of prime importance in criminal investigations but also in palaeontological work. Although sexual dimorphism (that is marked differences as between the general build of the two sexes) seems to have been very marked in ancient types of Man, it is less noticeable in many types of recent Man so that in some cases it is difficult to determine the sex of skeletal material. But long experience generally enables one to notice this or that perhaps inconspicuous feature which added to other indications suffices to indicate the sex. The female skull, indeed, is usually smaller than the male and also lighter. The calotte is (compared with the face) larger so that an impression of juvenility is conveyed, an impression increased by a more delicate facial skeleton, larger eye-sockets, smoother relief and less marked profile. The forehead of a woman's skull is usually less sloping, the glabella with the supraorbital region less developed and the mastoid process smaller.

The reconstruction of the head from the skull falls into two phases—the reproduction of the head itself and then the modelling of the facial mask. In the first phase comes the reconstruction of the most important masticatory and neck muscles with those of the shoulder. There is no doubt that the masticatory muscles can be accurately reconstructed. They are highly individual in size, volume and shape so that their form can be in each particular case determined from the skull.

For the second phase, that is to say the modelling of the facial mask, special training and long experience are necessary. The reproduction of the nose has always ranked as the most difficult task in facial reconstruction. As the nose consists mostly of cartilage and soft tissue, it presents, in the opinion of most anatomists and anthropologists, no reliable clues for reconstruction. But the reconstruction of mouth, eyes and ears must rank as still more complicated.

Now we offer some practical information about the reconstruction of individual facial features. Of course, we can only touch on certain points and do not claim to exhaust the subject.

The Nose

The construction of the nasal bones, the contour of the nasal opening, the configuration of the glabella, the structure of the whole supraorbitary region and of the outer corner of the eye together with the horizontal profile of the face, as well as the outer form of the alveolar region of the upper jaw, are all components which determine the shape of the soft parts of the nose. Therefore an examination of the nasal bones alone does not suffice for a reconstruction and is really pointless.

Undoubtedly the cartilaginous part of the nose and its soft parts form an organic continuation of the nasal bones, and the construction of the nasal bones determines, to a certain degree, the shape of the whole nose.

The main clue, then, for the reconstruction of the nose lies first of all in the nasal bones, the general shape of the piriform opening, the character of the sub-nasal section of the upper jaw process, that is to say the lower margin of the piriform opening, and the projecting point of the nasal bones.

Many years of work resulted in a reliable method for determining the nasal profile, in other words to 'fixing' the tip of the nose. The profile of the nose is projected by two straight lines, one at a tangent to the last third of the nasal bones and the other as a continuation of the main direction of the point of the bony nose. The point of intersection of these two lines will generally give the position of the tip of the nose.

The profile of the soft part of the nose, or the 'roof of the nose', is determined by the lateral margin of the piriform opening.

The form of the nasal openings depends directly on the shape of the lower and lateral form of the *apertura piriformis*. The tip of the nose is generally asymmetrically formed and of extremely variable shape. Its position, the details of its formation and the form of the subnasal margin of the piriform opening provide a sufficiently authentic model for the nasal openings. The height of the wings of the nose is influenced by the position of the *crista conchalis* of the lower muscle in the nasal opening.

The Mouth

The reproduction of the mouth is also tricky. Up to now anatomists have recognised no correlation between the soft parts which compose the mouth and the underlying portions of the facial skeleton. This can be explained by the fact that the mouth has, in reality, no direct connection with the skull. The mouth, indeed, consists mainly of the muscles which control its movements.

But in reconstructing the outer form of the mouth attention must be paid, of course, to the morphological peculiarities of the skull. The height and configuration of the alveolar portion of the upper jaw, the width of the dental arch, the size and shape of the teeth (the upper as well as the lower) and their occlusion—these are the main determinants from which the general form and the character of the details of the mouth can be recognised.

The teeth not only present important racial differences but they also show individual variations and definite indications of sex. At the present day one can observe a reduction in the molars. The last molar (wisdom tooth) shows a tendency to disappear.

For our work we found Lambert's observations on racial differences in the shape of teeth especially interesting. He noted that Negroes have large incisors. This confirms our own observations that the size (height of the enamel) of the incisors is associated with the thickness of the lips.

However, a series of observations conducted on the faces of

Negroes studying in the Soviet Union does not quite bear this out. Procheilia is not only associated with thickness and fullness of the lips but it has also other causes. It is generally accompanied by a greater or less prognathism of the jaws and incisors. With low teeth set upright no full-lipped mouth may be expected. On the other hand, even a slight prognathism of the jaws and teeth of moderate size will be accompanied by a full, soft mouth with marked procheilia and this form of mouth occurs frequently among European women.

The thickness of the mouth's soft parts depends on the relief of the jaw's alveolar processes, on the size, the height of the first incisors, the character of the dentition and the degree of prognathism. Loss of teeth and damage to those still in place strongly influence the outer form of the mouth. Cobblers, for instance, are accustomed to keep nails in their mouths and teeth constantly in contact with metal soon become scratched on their inner surfaces and then on their outer surfaces too, so that at last such teeth begin to split. Glass-blowers and players of wind instruments suffer comparable damage to their teeth—especially to the upper incisors.

Can the sex of an individual be determined from the dentition? The answer is probably 'Yes', though the problem is not fully solved. Anatomists and anthropologists, however, have for long recognised that a man's teeth are, in absolute volume, larger than a woman's. In relation, however, to general bodily proportions a woman's teeth are larger. It is further held that a man's teeth differ from a woman's not only in size but in shape. In a man's teeth the first incisor and the canine are, normally, of about the same height whereas the canine of the lower jaw is definitely higher.

The typical female dentition may be said to comprise large middle incisors and small canines in the upper jaw whereas the canines of the lower jaw are of about the same proportions as the second incisors. Generally speaking, of course, a woman's mandible is smaller, lighter and thinner than a man's, has a more rounded body, less marked relief, shorter rami etc.

Three types of facial profile are recognised:

1 Very marked projection (prognathism).

2 Medium projection (mesognathism).
3 Slight projection (orthognathism).

Prognathism may be natural or artificially induced. The first type occurs with many variations. In the case of double or complete prognathism, for instance, both jaws project so much that when the mouth is closed, the incisors of both jaws meet at a sharp angle. The lips are also very thick. This type is characteristic of equatorial races and is to be met with—though less often—among the Mongoloids of the south-east. By alveolar prognathism we understand a slight or medium projection of the jaw together with sharply projecting teeth. As a rule alveolar prognathism is, among Europeans and Mongoloids, not accompanied by procheilia of the lips. The mouth is often ugly and has a puckered appearance. The upper lip does not always cover the teeth.

Prognathism is generally very marked in Negroids, Polynesians, Malays and Papuans; it is also very common among Japanese (mostly in its alveolar form); it is less common among Chinese and Vietnamese and is still more rare among Mongols and the mongoloid peoples in the far north-east of the U.S.S.R.

Prognathism is relatively seldom met with among Europeans and when it does occur it is mostly in women.

Artificial prognathism is due most often to manipulation of the upper (and less often of the lower) jaw. Such deformation is dictated by traditional rites and ceremonies. It is easy to recognise.

We may recognise six types of bites:

1 Mandibular prognathism.
2 Labidontia.
3 Psallidontia.
4 Stegodontia.
5 Opisthodontia.
6 Chiathodontia.

These main types may also show variations due to anomalies but, generally speaking, such can be fairly easily recognised.

The normal forms may be briefly summarised as follows:

1 Mandibular prognathism. The incisors of the upper jaw close on those of the lower jaw so as to form an even surface. This form of bite is usually accompanied by procheilia of the lower lip and was characteristic of the early Europoids. Among

present-day populations of the U.S.S.R. mandibular prognathism is found among Jews, Armenians, Georgians and other peoples of the Caucasus. It is, however, very rare among recent mongoloid groups.

2 Labidontia. This is marked by total occlusion of the incisors and is very rare among present-day peoples. It occurs either with very marked prognathism or with extreme orthognathism. Labidontia is characteristic of European palaeolithic skulls as well as of neolithic skulls from eastern Europe and Siberia. In skulls from the Age of Metals it is seldom to be met with and I noticed it only very rarely among the northern Mongoloids, Buriats and inhabitants of the Altai region. In all cases it was accompanied by an extreme form of orthognathism. The mouth, with compressed lips, generally showed a pleasing pattern.

3 Psallidontia. This is the typical bite of recent populations and is rather seldom to be noted in the skulls of prehistoric Man. According to reports (which may not, perhaps, be very reliable) psallidontia is, at the present time, common among Chinese, Japanese and Negroes and very rare among Amerindians—it occurs hardly at all among Australian aboriginals. In psallidontia the upper lip is predominant.

4 Stegodontia occurs with prognathism of the jaws and with very marked projection of the incisors which are, however, generally set upright while the lower incisors lie behind the upper. Stegodontia is most common among Japanese and Chinese, less common among Mongols and rare among Europoids. It is certainly associated with procheilia of both lips.

5 Opisthodontia is characterised by alveolar prognathism of the upper incisors which project more than those of the lower jaw. This form of bite occurs, though only rarely, among Negroids, Mongoloids and Europoids. Opisthodontia is usually accompanied by marked procheilia and thick lower lips.

6 Chiathodontia. This gives the impression of being an anomaly but it is of frequent occurrence and appears, it would seem, in all recent racial groups. Generally chiathodontia is accompanied by prognathism of the jaw. Often there are gaps between the teeth which do not form a regular arch. The

mouth is mostly kept half-open and has an ugly appearance. Chiathodontia is common among many Europoids but with Mongoloids only among the Chinese and is seldom to be met with among Uzbeks. Although chiathodontia is usually accompanied by prognathism, no marked procheilia of the lips is to be observed. On the contrary, among Europoids at least this form of bite is associated with thin lips and even when chiathodontia occurs among Negroids the lips are not as full as with other types of bite. One gets the impression that with chiathodontia the lips are not as full as they should be and are stretched, as it were, in a vain effort to cover the teeth. The mouth always gapes a little and the incisors project from it. The reproduction of such a mouth is not difficult although its contour shows no definite pattern.

From all this it appears that despite the variety of their forms mouths can be modelled from the morphology of the jaws and teeth.

The Eyes

The eyes are the most expressive parts of the human visage. An artist can reproduce eyes in shape and colour and in their vividness. But can a sculptor reproduce the significance of the human eye? Can it in fact be represented in a reconstruction?

Does the incomparable expressiveness of the living eye lie in the glitter of the iris? No, apparently not.

The eyeball itself varies in size only to a very small extent from individual to individual. Its expressiveness depends on the details of the whole area around the eye—the shape of the eyelids, their folds, the size and shape of the eye-opening, the form of the eyelashes and so forth. The outer form of the eyelids varies greatly, or at least that of the upper lid does.

Can all the fine details of an eye be reproduced in a reconstruction? I think the answer is 'Yes'. For instance a certain relation has long been recognised between a low nasal root and the epicanthic fold—the so-called 'Mongoloid' or epicanthic fold is a peculiar form which more or less covers the tear-duct. Anthropologists not only note the presence of the ipicanthus as such but also its degree of development. In Europoid groups where 100 per cent of the children display a mongoloid fold, among adults of from twenty to twenty-five years old there can be noted a marked diminution in the number of cases, whereas in people over forty years old the epicanthus almost entirely disappears. With women the epicanthus is commoner than with men.

This observation leads us back to our first question—can the details of the eye be reproduced in a reconstruction? I think, 'Yes'. For long a certain connection between a low nasal root and the mongoloid fold has been recognised but among Negroids who have extremely low roots to their noses there is never any epicanthic fold. So it cannot be associated only with a depressed nasal root, indeed, it has been proved that there must also be present rounded, high, level and vertically only slightly projecting eye-sockets. With a combination of these features, lid-folds and epicanthus are very likely to occur.

A further very important detail of the eye is the opening of the eyelids and its form. It is well known that narrow openings are characteristic of the Mongoloid groups in central and eastern Asia. The eyelid opening varies very considerably with Europoid groups. A horizontally placed, wide eyelid-opening is typical of many equatorial and Negroid groups.

The outer form of the orbits determines almost all the important peculiarities of the shape of the eyes and eyelids. In order to depict rightly the form of the eyelids the shape of the margins of the orbits must be taken into account. The inner corner of the eye can be very reliably determined by the alveolar portion of the tear-duct region, but for the outer corner of the eye there seems to exist no clear clue.

The muscles surrounding the eyes are closely co-ordinated in their shape with the form and degree of development of the relief of the orbits, their general shape and position, the degree of projection of the eyeball and of its position. It is only by taking into account all these details that a correct reproduction of the outer form of the eye is possible.

The External Ear

It is difficult to say exactly why but it is a fact that the shape of the external ear has attracted Man's attention from remote ages. In the traditional lore of Indo-China an ear with a long lobe is held to be a sign of great wisdom. Aristotle considered long ears indicated an outstanding memory. Darwin referred to the human ear as a rudimentary organ.

In the middle of the last century the anatomist Maurelle noted abnormalities in the formation of the ears of degenerate individuals. Systematic studies have confirmed that the external ear is in shape, pattern and relief a peculiarly individual feature and the pattern of any given ear may be regarded (as are fingerprints) as absolutely unique to one person.

Although it is a difficult matter to describe a satisfactory method for reconstituting an external ear from the skull, still the individual variations in the construction of the temporal bones, the direction, size and shape of the auditory meatus, the form and relief of the mastoid process, as well as the main direction of the ascending ramus of the lower jaw, must be taken into account.

Thus the form of the external ear, its perpendicular axis, the degree of its projection from the head and even its approximate measurements, can be represented.

But many of the details of the ear's complicated relief—such as the shape of the lobes and of the tragus—must be 'intuitively' reconstructed.

4 *The Faces of Prehistoric Men*

The Age and the Evolution of Man

During a period of over thirty years about 200 reconstructions of prehistoric Man were made and from these the more important phases in the evolution of the species *Homo* can be seen. These reconstitutions were made from skulls and allow us to note that the changes from very primitive forms to those of the present day took place in an irregular sequence.

We should like to present here only some of the most interesting and important specimens which reflect in some measure the main phases of the evolutionary process, so that the reader may judge for himself how complicated it is. Each portrait allows not only individual traits to be recognised but also the main racial features of each type.

The portraits of primitive hominid forms from the lower Palaeolithic will occupy a considerable place, and then will follow reconstructions from the Upper Palaeolithic. Thus we will endeavour to keep to a chronological sequence although the varied evolutionary tempo of Man and his cultures will not always permit us to adhere strictly to this programme.

The method perfected in our laboratory has proved satisfactory despite the racial complications of the subject. Are we justified, however, in feeling so convinced that we can present an authentic portrait of prehistoric Man? The answer must be 'Yes'.

All the faces of Upper Palaeolithic Man can be reconstructed in just the same way as those of our contemporaries. When, however, we come to more primitive forms, these obviously do not permit such precise reproductions. We cannot ascertain reliably what were the soft parts of a Pithecanthropus or Neanderthaloid face and can only deduce their possible variations from the bone-relief of the skull. But will our suppositions correspond to reality? How can we find a means of verification? How should we proceed with the reconstitution of the appearance of prehistoric Man? Since we are not in a position to examine his soft parts can we then with tolerable certainty determine his outward morphological appearance?

In this connection we examined a number of heads of young chimpanzees and even undertook the reconstruction of that of a young male (from the skull). It was thus proved that in this extremely specialised anthropoid, the soft parts of the head approximated very closely to those of the human norm. It is true that the relief of a Neanderthaloid skull differs widely from that of a chimpanzee's with its sagittal and occipital crests as well as in the whole shape of the face and in the dentition. From this may be concluded that the Neanderthaloids were closely related to recent *Homo sapiens*. Undoubtedly the Pithecanthropoids occupy a place between the chimpanzee and the Neanderthaloids, although the first are clearly closer to the Neanderthaloids. Generally speaking, then, it must be concluded that the soft parts of earlier hominid forms must approximate to those of recent Man, that is to say must differ only a little from these latter.

The relief of the Neanderthaloid skull presents a number of specific features such as strongly developed supraorbital areas and glabella, a long face, high eye-orbits, a peculiarly formed flattened cheek-bone, an absence of mental eminence (chin) and strongly marked relief of the nape together with prominent protuberances at the back of the head, and a slightly developed mastoid process. There is a general incongruity between the massive facial skeleton and the low but elongated skull vault. These characteristic features must necessarily be reflected in the shape of the soft parts of the face and neighbouring areas. If we take into consideration the degree of variation in the supraorbital region and in the glabella of recent Man we know that with the increased thickness of these parts the underlying soft parts also are increased in thickness.

For the Neanderthaloids, Java Man (Pithecanthropoids) and Rhodesian Man the norms established for recent Man must be insufficient. But with the European Neanderthaloids and still more with the Mousterian Palestinian men with whom the glabella is but slightly marked, the soft parts clearly fall within the maximum limits—or perhaps a little more—of recent Man.

In the reproduction of facial details we proceed from the morphological foundation of the skull structure and use the methods whose principles we have described already.

It is clear that reconstructions from the skulls of most ancient Man can prove less individualised than reconstructions of the faces of contemporaries, but there is no reason to doubt the authenticity of the former.

In view of the numerous discoveries of recent years and the perfecting of methods of research, we can hardly be satisfied with the conceptions prevailing hitherto about the evolution of *Homo sapiens,* both in general and in particular as shown in the conventional tables of cultural development. In fact, the question as to how and how quickly the evolution of recent Man from earlier types occurred must be posed anew, We know, for instance, that not all early forms of Man participated to a like degree in the production of *Homo sapiens*. The once accepted sequence Pithecanthropoids, Neanderthaloids, *Homo sapiens* is not in accord with recent knowledge. We possess a number of undoubted proofs for the contemporaneous existence of Pithecanthropoids, the so-called 'classical' Neanderthaloids and early forms of recent Man.

The antiquity of the classical Neanderthaloids has been reckoned at between 75,000 and 40,000 years. However, not so highly specialised forms of Neanderthaloids (such as Steinheim) are much older—and date back to some 300,000 years. There are sites where undisturbed Mousterian strata overlie early Aurignacian. And, finally, we know of remains of recent Man which are accompanied by Mousterian industry.

All this tends to prove that anthropogenesis and the evolution of cultures are exceedingly complicated matters. It is not our business here to recommend universally valid schemes especially as such schemes are hardly possible. The abundance of local forms in the industries of cultures existing side by side, the irregular and complicated course of Man's evolution and the difference in the rate of evolution of earlier and existing races, all prevent the construction of a system universally valid. Nevertheless, we must keep to a certain sequence if we want to present the reader with a chronological account of the different phases of evolution.

We must probably assume that Man's history began over a million years ago. The first divisions of Palaeolithic culture were established by the French archaeologist Gabriel de Mortillet who in the year 1869 published his sequence of Mousterian, Solutrean and Magdalenian. In 1885 Mortillet enlarged his system and in the

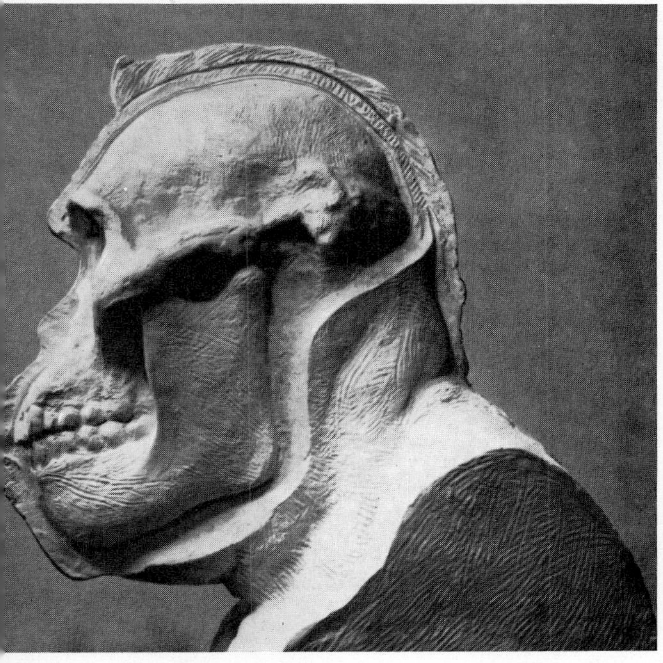

From several casts the skull of a young female Plesianthropus was selected for reproduction (*below*). The soft parts were copied from those of a chimpanzee. The nose was small and seemed to be depressed between the eyes and the heavy, strongly projecting lower part of the face. The mouth was very large and wide with thin, flattened ape-like lips (*above*). Despite a certain resemblance to the hominids, the Plesianthropus really appears to come closer to the recent anthropoids.

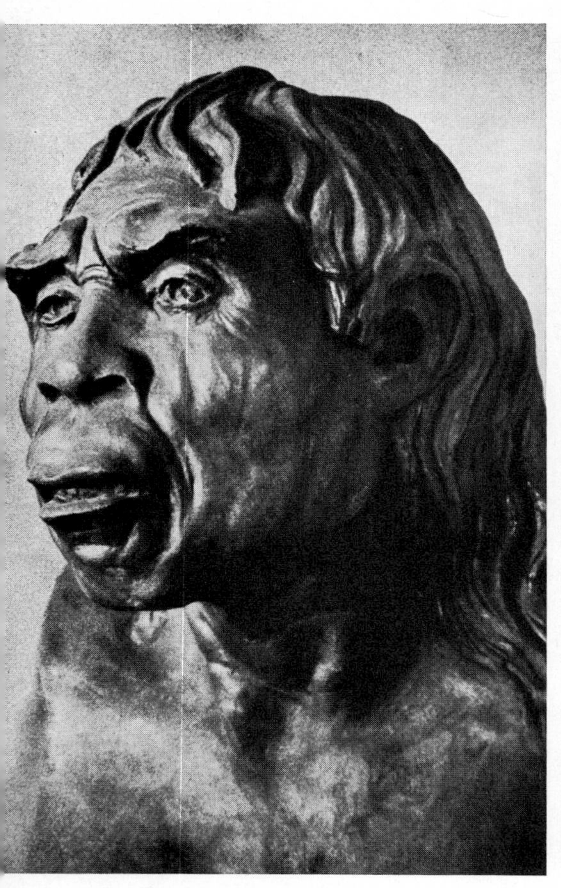

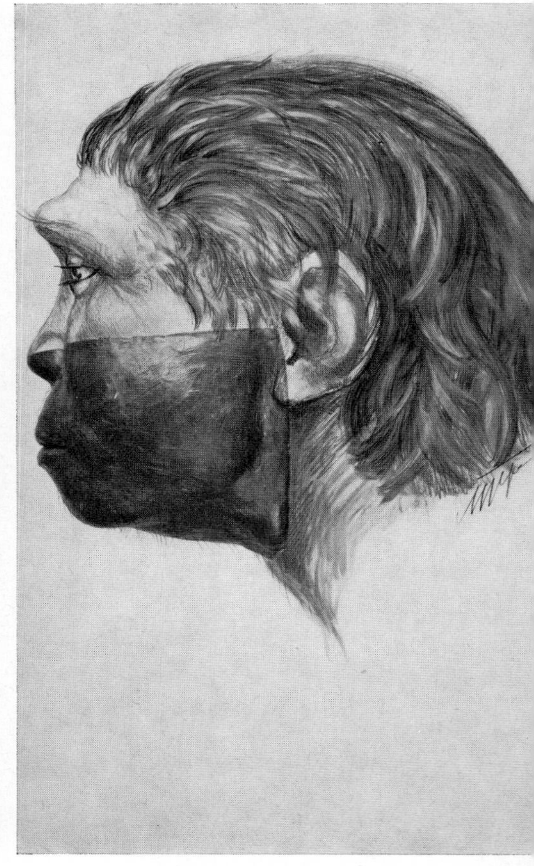

In Mid Pleistocene times, about 350,000 years ago, there lived in what is now north China a group of ancient fore-runners of recent Man – the *Sinanthropi* or *Pithecanthropi pekinenses* (*above left, reconstruction*). The sinanthropes lived in caves, walked upright, knew the use of fire and made and used artefacts of quartzite, diabase and flint.
(*Above right*) An attempted reconstruction of the head of Heidelberg Man of whom only the lower jaw exists.

The Steinheim woman (*opposite page right and left above*) was nearer to recent Man than the Neanderthaloids of the 'classical' type although she lived long before them (in the Mindel-Riss Inter-glacial period – that is some 200,000 years ago).
The Le Moustier youth (*opposite page below*) was a typical Neanderthaloid. This type was wide-spread over Europe, western Asia and north Africa.

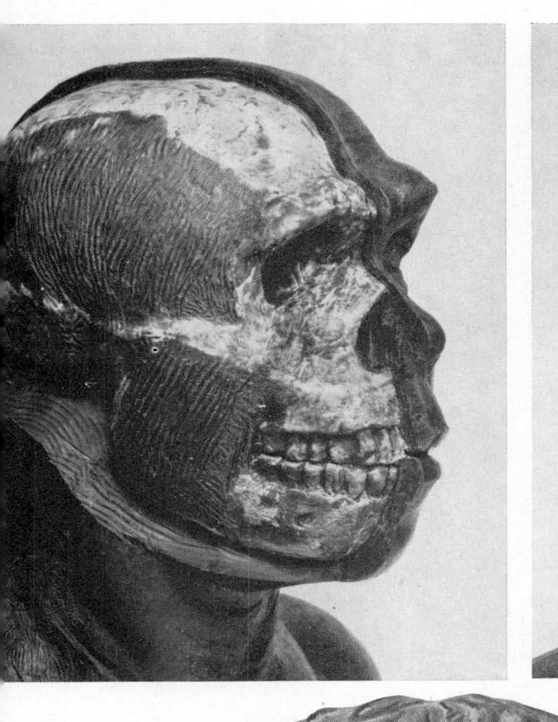
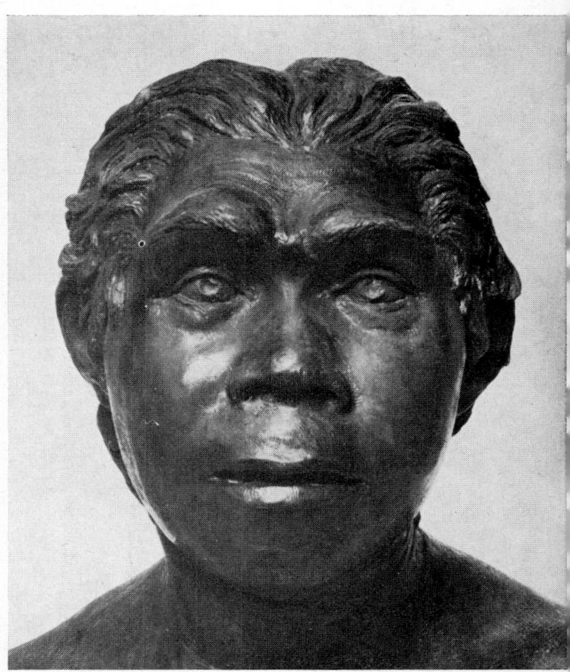
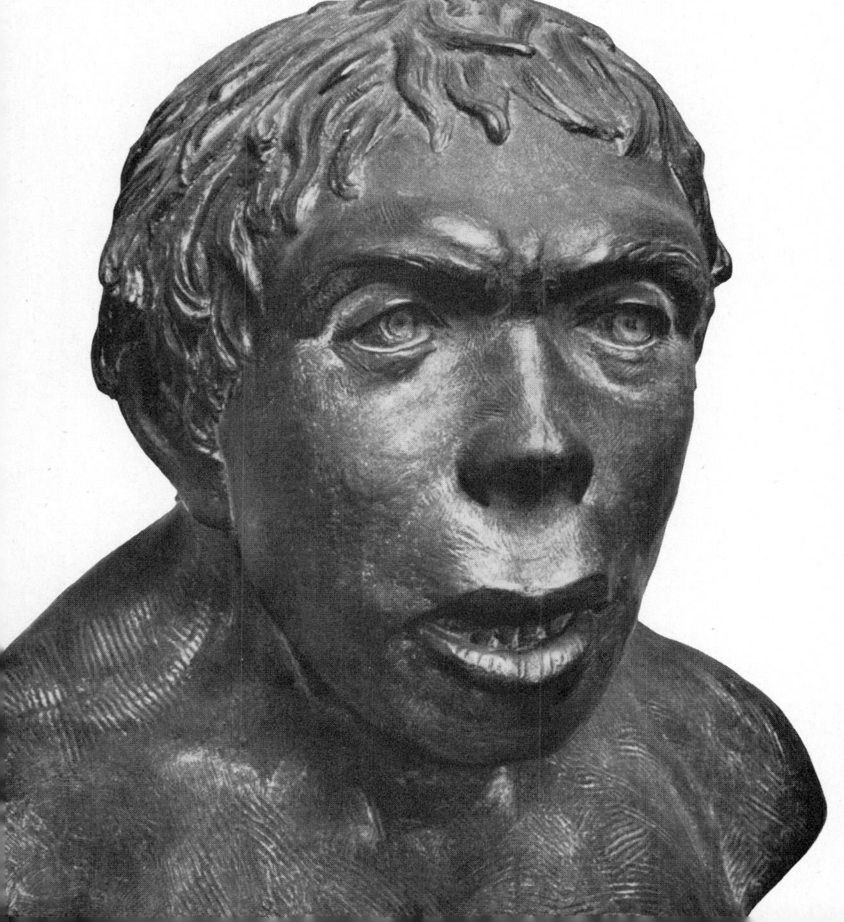

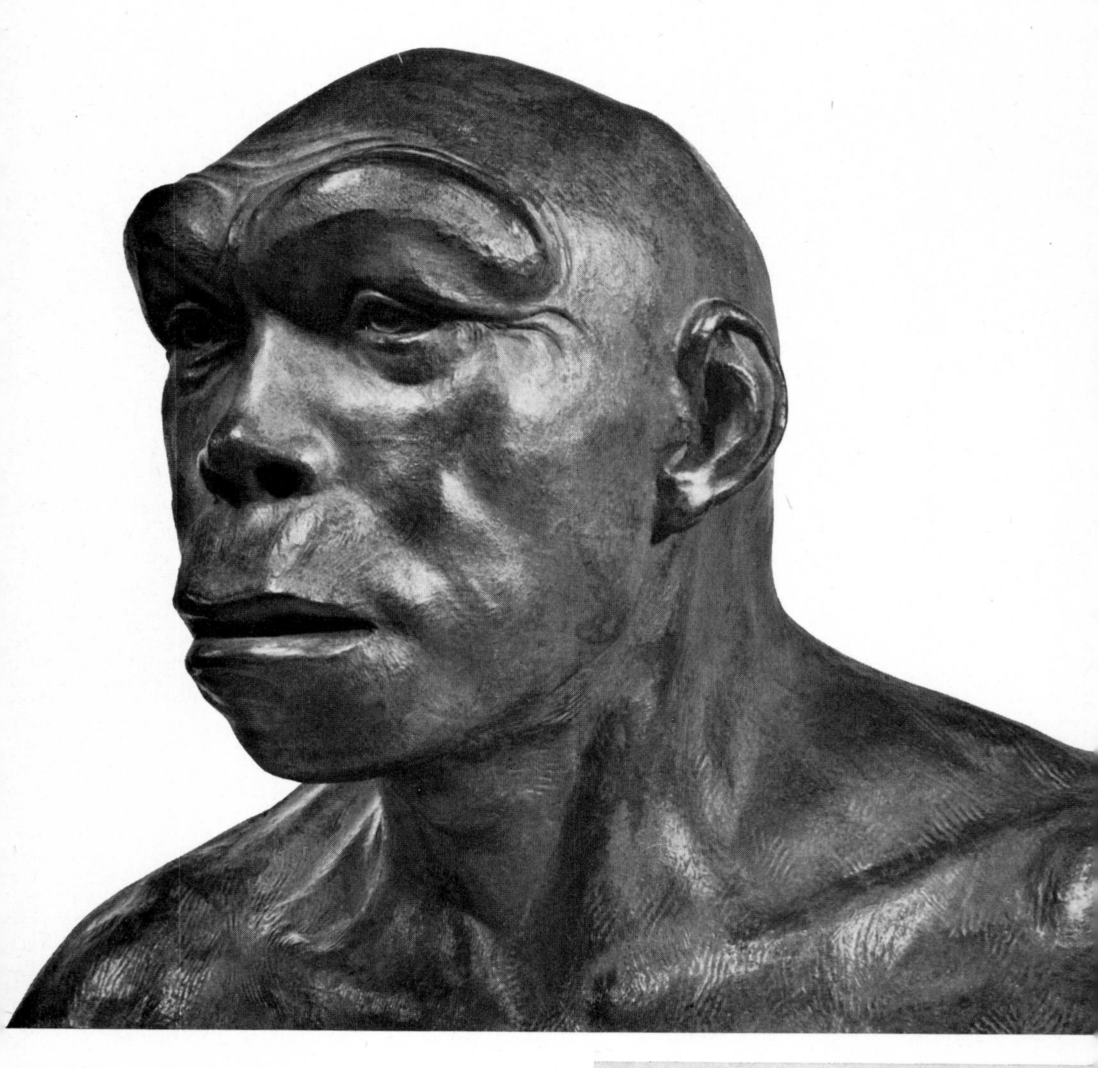

Rhodesian Man (*right*). The outlines of the skull with an indication of the soft parts. (*Above*) The reconstruction of the head which shows a peculiar combination of very primitive features together with those of a progressive type.

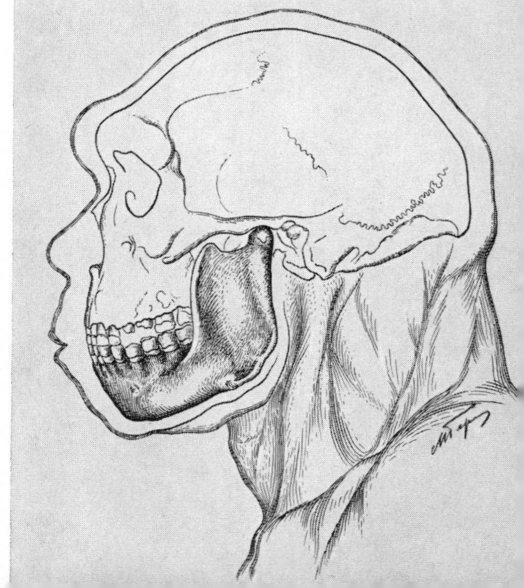

second edition of his book *La Prehistoire Antiquité de l'Homme* he inserted the Acheulian between the Chellean and the Mousterian. Later the Abbé Breuil rectified this classification by the insertion of the Aurignacian between the Mousterian and the Solutrean. And then Edgar Piette found at the Mas d'Azil site (the foothills of the Pyrenees) a transition culture above the Magdalenian and leading to the Neolithic, which he called Azilian (Mesolithic).

There are now in western and eastern Europe numerous sites dating from the Upper Palaeolithic, but the material recovered from them no longer justifies us in regarding the classification hitherto adopted as valid for all the Old World. In fact the local variations in Upper Palaeolithic cultures are so considerable that a revision of the classifications has undoubtedly become necessary. But this does not mean that a generally valid scheme just cannot be produced but merely that cultural evolution in prehistoric Asia and Africa developed at a different rate from that of Europe.

The similarities between the most ancient industries are to be attributed not only to common centres of diffusion but also to the conditions of life in which early Man existed. As early as the Acheulian local variations of artefact-types appear, while in the Mousterian, successive phases of development can be recognised in cultural areas which are often quite close to one another. In the Upper Palaeolithic quite clearly differentiated cultural provinces can be noticed.

It is noteworthy that in their succession the cultures are not only renewed but also become more and more complicated. This holds good especially for western Europe. For instance, from Mortillet's time the earliest stage of the Lower Palaeolithic bore the name of Chellean. Today this designation is often changed to 'Abbevillian' (from Abbeville in the French department of the Somme since there this very ancient industry is more fully represented).

Very often contemporary with the Chellean a parallel variety of lower Palaeolithic artefacts is found known as Clactonian, (from Clacton in Essex). The Clactonian technique of flint flaking differs from the Chellean. The main artefacts of the Chellean and the Acheulian is the hand-axe while the Clactonian on the other hand is characterised by artefacts prepared from flakes. From the Clactonian there developed, during the Acheulian, the Levalloisian which later evolved parallel to the classical Mousterian.

In France where first the Aurignacian and the Solutrean were recognised there is now distinguished another cultural phase—the Perigordian. In Germany instead of the Solutrean we have the Gravettian as also in Czechoslovakia where the Mousterian is followed by another culture, the Szelettian. Russian archaeologists have demonstrated that many Upper Palaeolithic cultures in the area of the eastern European plains are to be regarded as co-existing.

No less complicated is the problem of the geological age of the Palaeolithic cultures.

The whole of Man's history lies in the Quaternary period, that is to say the last phase of the modifications of the earth's surface. As long as our planet has existed it has undergone a complicated process of change. During the Quaternary outlines of continents varied, mountain masses and plateaux arose, the hydrosphere shifted its position. Glaciers were formed, spread and then retreated. The whole landscape was several times subjected to transformations. Warmth-loving flora developed and then disappeared to give place to coniferous forests, cold, dry steppes and even tundra. The animal world too adapted itself to these changes.

As the Mindel glaciation retreated there appeared in central Europe deciduous woods and savannas where animals from the warm zone were able to flourish—the southern elephant *(Elephas meridionalis)*, the Etruscan rhinoceros *(Rhinoceros etruscus)* and even the hippopotamus *(Hippopotamus amphibius)*. During these many changes Man's cultures developed at an increasing rate. Gradually Man's physical appearance also changed. In the first phases of Man's evolution nature's demands played an especially great role and determined not only the rate of that evolution in Man's body but also in his culture. Sometimes it was hastened and sometimes it was slowed down.

So it could also happen that surroundings—in the widest sense of that word—through isolation not only furthered the biological specialisation of the human being and slowed down the development of his culture but even steered him for a time or for ever away from the general course of evolution and development.

During the last decade geological and stratigraphical researches into the Quaternary deposits of Europe, Asia, Africa and Australia have shown that the stratigraphy of Villefranche and the scheme of the glaciation successions derived from the Alps are applicable only to certain regions, and although they were formerly universally accepted, they cannot be regarded as valid all over the world.

Despite the complicated nature of the problem, we shall in this book have to confine ourselves to a slightly modernised version of the Alpine scheme of glacial deposits: thus, I Gunz, II Mindel, III Riss and IV Würm glaciations connected up with cultural phases and the corresponding discoveries of the remains of prehistoric Man. What we will endeavour to do is to help the reader to visualise the antiquity and the duration of this or that cultural period—at least in its main lines . . . and to recognise also the chronological position of the various early hominid forms.

But we make no claim to absolute accuracy or inclusiveness. Thus, almost all the recent and most revealing finds in Africa have not been taken into account, since we have not had at our disposal complete descriptions of these discoveries nor have we had available casts of bones and skull fragments.

5 *The Australopithecines*

The Pliocene and the earlier part of the Pleistocene were epochs in which there was a marked diffusion of anthropoid apes. The area they inhabited was much larger than that of their present-day homes. They were for the most part tree-dwellers and it would seem more or less at home in open spaces and as their skeletons show they could move about on their two legs. They were probably omnivorous but perhaps for preference flesh-eaters. This may be regarded as proved for South African apes and most probably also holds good for the giant apes of south China, which owing to their huge size could not live an arboreal life. Even so specialised an animal as the orang-utan, pre-eminently a tree-dwelling creature, sometimes has to live on the ground and in caves. Possibly the Pliopithecines were not arboreal animals either.

All these very ancient apes differ from existing ones in several features but show resemblances to them, especially to the apes which live in the same areas as did the very ancient forms. So, for instance, the Pliopithecus of Ertemte comes in its bodily build very near to the gibbon, the fossil orang-utans resemble the existing ones and the Australopithecus is most like the chimpanzee and gorilla.

Many archaeologists and anthropologists—apparently more on the grounds of analogy than from irrefutable proof—would see the original home of Man in Africa. Highly interesting discoveries have been made. Artefacts of pre-Chellean type have been found, many skull bones of fossil anthropoids and remains of early Man have been discovered, the latter sometimes accompanied by Chellean or Acheulian artefacts. These discoveries have undoubtedly strengthened the theory of Man's African origin.

The Taung Child

In 1924 near the railway-station of Taung, in the eastern part of the Kalahari Desert (South Africa), a skull was uncovered during work in a limestone quarry. As was obvious from the teeth it belonged to an individual aged from three to four years. All the milk teeth were present but the first four permanent teeth had only just begun to erupt. The skull was not complete. There remained only the facial bones, the lower jaw and the frontal bone. Infiltration of mineral salts had formed a cast of the skull cavity and had cemented the bones together. Thus an almost complete picture of the skull could be obtained. The cranial capacity was about 390 cubic centimetres. The anthropologists Gregory and Hellmann were firmly of the opinion that the skull, from its construction, occupied a place between an anthropoid ape and a primitive Man.

I utilised a plaster cast of this Australopithecine skull. It was not very difficult to supply the missing portions of the skull-vault. For the reproduction of the soft parts I utilised measurements of the soft parts of a young chimpanzee (aged three to five years) as well as those from children of from three to four years old. The ear was modelled on that of a chimpanzee as well as the covering of hair.

What appeared was the portrait of a little ape, which was undoubtedly closer to Man than any apes existing today.

A Female Plesianthropus

In 1936 and 1943 in the now famous Sterkfontein cave near Johannesburg, among numerous mammalian bones, twelve almost complete anthropoid skulls were discovered, together with many other bones of apes—vertebrae, ribs, iliac bones, bones of the upper thigh, a tibia, wrist bones, phalanges and teeth.

From this material it was possible to reconstitute the appearance of these apes and even a detailed reproduction of their anatomy.

The apparent height of the female Plesianthropus was about 122 centimetres. The male must have been taller, probably (according to Broom) about 152 centimetres. The cranial capacity varied between 422 and 500 cubic centimetres. Despite a certain resemblance to Man in a number of features, the Plesianthropus—as the construction of the skull and the size of the brain showed—stood undoubtedly nearer to the existing apes than to Man.

We had at our disposal several casts of Plesianthropus skulls and I chose the most complete. It was that of a young female but it was in fragments. Especially regrettable was the complete lack of teeth—and there was no lower jaw. But the remaining fragments of tooth-roots in the sockets of the upper jaw allowed us to fix approximately the size and position of the different teeth. From these the teeth of the lower jaw could be reproduced schematically.

For the reconstitution of the lower jaw there served as clues the shape of the temporal bones, the form of the temporal fossa, the size and shape of the zygomatic bone, as well as the degree of projection and the height of the alveolar portion of the upper jaw. Of course we took into account details of formation from the jaw fragments of other specimens of Plesianthropus.

The well-preserved muscle-relief of the temporal fossa and of the lower margin of the zygomatic bone indicated a correspondingly marked relief of the outer surface of the lower jaw. The reconstructed mandible had a massive body, narrow, high rami and no traces of a mental eminence.

The relief of the base of the skull, the position of the foramen magnum, the size and position of the mastoid process, as well as the occipital condyles indicated an upright position of the Plesianthropus. The neck was obviously short and the shoulders sloping ape-fashion.

The Plesianthropus skull was more like that of the chimpanzee than that of any other of the existing apes. The calvaria had about the same form, the face, however, was relatively more massive and had an especially heavy lower jaw and in this feature the Plesianthropus more resembled the orang-utan.

The reconstruction of the Plesianthropus head was made by taking into account the thickness of a chimpanzee's soft parts. The relatively low and but slightly projecting orbits and the strongly marked supraorbital region indicated the shape of the deeply sunk ape-like eyes. The narrow almost flat nasal bones, their shape and the small nasal aperture showed the form of the soft parts of the nose which was very small, not wide, and seemed to be depressed between the eyes and under the strongly projecting region above them. The mouth was large with thin, flattened ape-like lips.

The Pithecanthropi

In the year 1891 the Dutch army surgeon Eugen Dubois discovered in the valley of the Solo river (Java) in a Lower Pleistocene level numerous fossil bones of animals, among which were a few remains of a man-like creature which he named *Pithecanthropus erectus*, that is 'upright ape-man'. The bones—a brain-case and a femur—displayed together with obviously very primitive characters, some man-like features.

From 1937 to 1940 the Dutch scientist von Königswald found two further calvarias, a lower jaw and a few teeth of Pithecanthropus—these were unearthed on the banks of the Djetmoro, a tributary of the Solo. A thorough examination of the whole collection showed that the bones must have belonged to seven individuals. To judge from the length of the ribs the Pithecanthropi must have stood at least 170 centimetres tall. The largest recorded cranial capacity of the living apes is 660 cubic centimetres; that of the Pithecanthropi was from 850 to 900 cubic centimetres and therefore in volume the latter was more man-like.

Java Man most probably used artefacts of Chellean type (as did the cognate form the *Atlanthropus* of North Africa), but despite all efforts it has proved impossible to discover any. The pithecanthropoid bones were all found in the same geological formation and associated with a rich fauna—stegodon, elephant, Indian rhinoceros, tapir, wild boar, stag, buffalo and cats. The stratigraphy of the finds and the type of fauna would justify our placing the Pithecanthropus in about the middle of the Lower Pleistocene; that would mean that he flourished about 500,000 years ago.

For the reconstitution of the Pithecanthropus face we used Weinert's reconstruction somewhat modified in the light of most recent evidence, for Weinert undertook his work as long ago as the early 'twenties, before the discovery of the Sinanthropus and other pithecanthropoid skulls. He had then at his disposal only the cranial vault and the teeth found by Dubois. Nevertheless, Weinert's reconstruction was carried out with great care and precision. We are, however, of the opinion that, in view of the degree of evolution of the skull's relief, the mastoid process should not be as strongly marked as Weinert indicated. Probably, also the general prognathism of the face was rather less, the eye-orbits rather higher, the cheek-bones thinner and the lower jaw not so heavy.

In making these modifications we took into account such discoveries of recent years as the Sinanthropus bones, the Steinheim skull, the Heidelberg jaw and the mandibles of Atlanthropus.

For the reconstruction of the female Pithecanthropus head we assumed the thickness of the soft parts to be very nearly that in modern Man and only in the glabella region did we make a modification.

The skull of Pithecanthropus IV cannot claim to be quite authentic since it was reconstituted by Weidenreich from very incomplete elements. Königswald had discovered separate skull fragments which could not all have belonged to one individual. Furthermore there was among them none of the upper part of the face or of the frontal bone.

Weidenreich had undoubtedly taken into account all the resources of comparative anatomy. The reconstruction of Pithecanthropus IV which he undertook makes a very convincing impression. Compared with Pithecanthropus I and II, Weidenreich's skull is larger, has bigger mastoid processes, and deeper fossae while the foramen magnum occupies a central position. Furthermore the skull presents a number of features which might cause it to be regarded as of a peculiar sort of Pithecanthropus.

In view of the morphological peculiarities of the Pithecanthropus skulls, we may assume that sexual dimorphism was about as strongly marked as in living chimpanzees. We consider the Pithecanthropus skull IV as that of a male and skull I as that of a female.

6 The Chellean and Heidelberg Man

The most ancient stone artefacts fashioned by Man in the earliest phases of his evolution were so primitive, shapeless and undifferentiated that it is often difficult to distinguish them from chips and flakes due to natural causes.

Perhaps the most ancient undoubted artefacts date from the Chellean. This culture-phase was named by Mortillet from the classical site on the eastern edge of the town of Chelles (in the Seine et Marne department) and a short distance to the east of Paris. The plateau adjoining Chelles is composed of very ancient gravels of coarse sands deposited by the Marne river which here form a thick conglomerate. The stratum reaches a thickness of about 25 feet and above it lie younger gravels and sands.

In the lowest level were found Chellean artefacts together with the bones of ancient and southern elephant (*Elephas antiquus* and *Elephas meridionalis*), hippopotamus (*Hippopotamus amphibius*) and Merck's rhinoceros (*Rhinoceros merckii*), as well as of other animals.

In the upper levels lay artefacts of Acheulian and Mousterian workmanship. However primitive and coarse the Chellean implements may seem, there can be no doubt that they are differentiated tools with various uses.

Typical of the Chellean are large hand-axes with bifacially chipped blades. But hand-axes were not the only artefacts of the Chellean, there were also many of small implements fashioned from flakes of various sizes.

It is certain that besides stone artefacts simple wooden instruments were in use as bludgeons, hunting spears and so forth.

The Chellean culture extended over a huge space of time—at least 200,000 years—from about the end of the Gunz glaciation (II) until the Mindel-Riss Interglacial.

In this period Man was settled in a very extensive area of the Old World, as is evident from many discoveries made in various parts of Africa, Asia and southern Europe.

In 1907 during work in a sand-pit near the village of Mauer not far from Heidelberg there was unearthed a primitive-looking human mandible. The anthropologist Schoetensack gave the specimen the name *Homo beidelhargensis*. The jaw lay at a depth of 14·10 metres and was associated with a typical Mindel II fauna—

mostly of Etruscan rhinoceros and ancient elephant. Near where the jaw was found were no artefacts or traces of hearths.

The Heidelberg mandible displays a very complicated construction. Its contours in no way resemble those of an ape-jaw but there are also present a number of features far removed from those in recent Man. The jaw is clearly very primitive but not so specialised as that of an ape. There is no projection of a chin or indeed any mental eminence (i.e. chin formation), the body of the jaw is massive, the ascending ramus is not only very broad but peculiarly formed, it looks neither like that of an ape nor of a recent Man. The dental arch is absolutely like our own as are the teeth although rather larger.

But what did the most ancient Men look like? Can we form an idea of his outward appearance?

We tried to give an answer to these questions. We started of course from the lower jaw and reconstructed the upper jaw and this served as a foundation for the lower part of this face. All these parts were modelled in plastic. The whole upper part of the face and the head must be regarded as hypothetical and was therefore only drawn and not modelled. The Heidelberg Man shows a similarity to the Steinheim woman whose remains are to be dated to the transition between Chellean and Acheulian cultures. Morphologically speaking the Heidelberg and Steinheim specimens were probably much alike.

The Acheulian and the Steinheim Woman

The Acheulian follows on the Chellean and is named from the site of Saint Acheul near to Amiens on the Somme river.

It can clearly be seen at the classical sites how the Chellean culture gradually gave way to the more evolved Acheulian. In the lowest levels lie typical Chellean artefacts. Then, above, the old implement forms are replaced by new and more perfected ones that are typical of the Acheulian. The smaller objects assume pronounced shapes and their uses are clearly differentiated.

During the Acheulian there developed step by step new methods of artefact production and another technique of stone-knapping came into use. The pace of the culture's development obviously increased. The late Acheulain can be recognised by the increase in the number of microlithic artefacts—points, triangular and oval disks. The developed small implements of the Micoquian stage also appear. At the end of the Acheulian appears a new technique, the Levalloisian (see p. 66).

During the excavation of a gravel-pit, a quaternary terrace was cut into. This was formed of deposits laid down by the Murr, a tributary of the Neckar, and in them quite by chance there was unearthed a hominid skull, which later came to be known as the Steinheim skull. The year was 1933.

The skull lay more than seven metres (about 22 feet) down in a gravel deposit. Above the skull was the tooth of an ancient elephant and just under the skull portions of the skeleton of a Merck's rhinoceros. These faunal remains indicate a Mindel-Riss Interglacial date for the hominid cranium. Since no artefacts were found nearby it is not possible to give a more precise dating although it may be safest to attribute the Steinheim specimen to the first half of the Acheulian, say, some 200,000 years ago.

The skull was badly damaged. The whole left side of the brain-case was pushed in and a considerable portion of it missing. The facial skeleton was a good deal deformed. No incisors, canines or premolars were found. The right cheek-bone and part of the neighbouring articulations were lacking and the base of the skull was destroyed. For our reconstruction we had only a plaster cast.

First of all the missing parts of the skull must be reconstituted and then the lower jaw modelled. It was massive with a short, wide ramus and retreating chin. After the reconstruction the skull appeared as small, long, with low cranial vault, relatively high but retreating forehead and a coarse, projecting supraorbital region. The nose was only slightly projecting, the eye orbits were small, the alveolar area was high, the cheek-bones differed in form definitely from that of the Neanderthaloids. Owing to this peculiarity the Steinheim skull shows a close resemblance to that of *Homo sapiens*. The reconstructed lower jaw as seen in profile recalled by its contour that of Heidelberg Man. But the dental arch was different in the two skulls.

For the reconstruction of the soft parts we relied on measurements from living men but modified them by taking into account the pronounced development of the glabella and the supraorbital regions.

The skull was obviously that of a woman, but the reconstructed face did not show much feminine softness. But despite her great age of some 200,000 years, the Steinheim woman much more resembles *Homo sapiens* than she does the classical Neanderthaloids of Europe, although she must have lived long before them.

Many authorities incline to the opinion that this but slightly specialised form of *Archanthropus* displays just those characteristics which may have led later to *Homo sapiens*—through bypassing the classical Neanderthal stage.

But it is also possible that the Steinheim skull represents a very ancient human form that later developed in two directions. One line, for reasons unknown to us, may have evolved in isolation and have led by biological specialisation to the classical Neanderthaloids.

As milestones on this road we might regard the following specimens—Mauer, Steinheim, Ehringsdorf, Krapina, Le Moustier, La Quina, La Chapelle, etc.

The other direction taken may have been a less isolated one, and have consisted of southern groups of Man who lived in closer contact with each other on the sea-coasts. Their way may have led, owing to continuous contacts and biological admixture, to a development resulting in the appearance of recent Man. Admittedly this path is indicated by fewer discoveries. It might, however, have had as milestones Mauer, Steinheim, the apparently hybrid Mousterian men in Palestine, the Staroselie, Grimaldi, Combe-Capelle specimens, etc.

The schemes, however, can only be presented as very hypothetical. They need much special study and extensive and profound checking from the evidence. A definite solution of the problem must await a much greater number of archaeological and palaeontological discoveries than we possess at the present time.

The Sinanthropus

During the first parts of the Acheulian there lived in what is now northern China ancient ancestors of recent Man—the *Sinanthropi*. Not far from the village of Choukoutien about forty miles to the south-west of Peking, in the years from 1927 to 1937 remains and many artefacts were discovered.

The Chinese scientist Pei Wenchung discovered in a cave two *Sinanthropus* skulls. From 1937 more bones were unearthed which altogether must have come from at least forty different individuals of *Sinanthropus* type—isolated teeth as well as the split bones of men, women and children. All the bones were found in one and the same spot together with fossil animal remains and stone implements. The site is a deep cleft in the karst formation which was filled in with refuse and extensive successive layers of ash and charcoal. The hominid bones were scattered about throughout the length and breadth of the cave's fillings.

The accompanying fossil bones of animals indicate the kind of climate in which the *Sinanthropus* lived. It was milder and damper than the local climate of today. The very numerous animal fossils belong to a Middle Pleistocene fauna—cave bear (*Ursus spelaeus*), hyena (*Hyaena sinensia*), sabre-toothed feline (*Machairodus*), elephant (*Elephas namadieus*), buffalo (*Bubalus teilhardi*) and rhinoceros (*Rhinoceros mercki*).

The *Sinanthropus* industry consisted mostly of local stone, fine-grained, hard greenish sandstone, quartzite, disbase but not often of flint. The chipping technique was clearly defined and regular. The artefacts consist mostly of bifacial implements prepared from flakes. In fact one gets the impression that this industry resembles the Clactonian in the method of manufacture. There were, however, at Choukoutien, points, scrapers and other forms suggesting a relation with the Acheulian.

Since for a reconstruction of the *Sinanthropus* we disposed only of some of the principal bones—and these in the form of plaster casts—we endeavoured, with this not quite satisfactory material, to reconstruct the *Sinanthropus* skull. In this way we produced a male and female adult.

The female agreed in almost all respects with the skull reconstructed by Weidenreich, and although I worked with copies of the individual bones I took Weidenreich's reconstruction as the basis for my further work. The female skull had a long though low vault, a narrow, retreating forehead and a markedly projecting back to the head but with the upper part of the occipital bone considerably flattened. The forehead was very narrow, the region over the eyes projected strongly and the glabella area but slightly developed.

The face was not very long, the eye-sockets and the cheek-bones were rather flattened, the nasal bones were not very projecting and the jaw prognathous. The mandible was massive, had a retreating chin and a broad ramus. This combination of features lent the skulls a definitely primitive character.

With the *Sinanthropus* sexual dimorphism was more marked than in recent Man and probably was comparable to that observable in chimpanzees. The male skull possessed a more marked relief, with larger mastoid processes and a more massive facial skeleton. The mandible was especially heavy. For the reconstruction we utilised the mean measurements of the soft parts in recent Man and modified these only where the skull relief was exceptionally marked.

Many authorities are of the opinion that the *Sinanthropus* lived mainly by gathering but that his diet also included small animals he managed to catch—such as reptiles, amphibians, rodents, birds and their eggs. That Peking Man hunted larger game, these authors would not admit, although near the *Sinanthropus* remains many animal bones were found. It was assumed rather that these Palaeolithic men ate animals which had died naturally.

There exists reasons for supposing that these men of the Old Stone Age already possessed a primitive form of speech which perhaps might be called 'signal language', that is to say the *Sinanthropus* made use of a small number of simple sounds and signs for communication with one another. It is only in such conditions that joint action in hunting, the preparation of implements and the collection of fuel are imaginable.

Morphologically the *Sinanthropi* were closely connected with the Pithecanthropoids so that they can be included in one and the same group. None the less Peking Men were different from the Pithecanthropoids and doubtless possessed a more highly developed brain, they possessed useful working tools, they utilised fire and they probably knew how to converse.

However, despite these progressive features, the mode of life of Peking Man was still very primitive.

The Mousterian and the Neanderthaloids

The Mousterian is not a homogeneous culture phase in the sense that with the passage of time local evolutionary types developed. Clearly the so-called 'classical' Mousterian is linked with the Acheulian, but there exist various sites even in western Europe (of Mousterian culture) where the predominance of the Levallois technique may be recognised. In eastern Europe such sites seem, indeed, to be in the majority. Probably, however, what we have here is not a case of chronological sequence between earlier and later phases of one and the same culture but rather historically conditioned, local varieties of the same cultural phase.

The Mousterian begins in the Riss glaciation II and lasts right through the Riss-Würm Interglacial and Würm glaciation I, so it extends over an immense span of time. In places the Mousterian is found to be contemporary with the first traces of the Upper Palaeolithic.

The end of the Acheulian and the beginning of the Mousterian was a time of warm and dry climate. Over much of Europe the southern elephant and Merck's rhinoceros were found while farther south there were even hippopotamuses. Great herds of horses, aurochs and bison roamed over central Europe.

Skull fragments dating from the very beginning of the Mousterian were found in the Ilm Valley travertine (near Weimar); they are known as the Ehringsdorff skull. From Saccopastore (not far from Rome) comes a skull that should be more or less contemporary with that of Ehringsdorff but which is obviously younger. The finds made in the Krapina rockshelter on the Krapnice river (Yugoslavia) are dated to the beginning of the Old Mousterian. To all appearances also the skeleton from the Kiik-Koba grotto in the Crimea is also to be dated to this same period or to one very near it.

The period of the developed Mousterian coincides in Europe with the Würm glaciation. It was an epoch that was very harsh and hard for early Man and must have tried his resistance sorely since he possessed only very primitive implements and yet he had to do as best he could to shelter from the assaults of nature. Only very gradually did he develop specific qualities which made his struggle for existence easier. Such specialisation had as a result the separation and the isolation of the human communities—that at least is our supposition. With Man's biological adaptation went a slow development of the classical Mousterian culture.

There is no doubt that the Neanderthaloids not only knew fire but made plentiful use of it. They could keep it and take it about with them and even knew how to kindle it.

The stone industry affords proof that the Neanderthaloids knew how to work wood and how to prepare objects such as cudgels, hunting spears and javelins and could even fashion very primitive shelters. Bone implements also existed but almost exclusively in the form of points from splinters. The Mousterian men used bones but mainly for the working of stone artefacts, indeed they used the bones as anvils and with their help prepared retouched blades.

Mousterian men lived by hunting small and big game and from an extensive gathering activity. In the Mousterian sites one comes across the most varied sorts of animal bones, the booty of prehistoric hunters. In the zone of the coniferous and mixed-forest tundra the most frequent are the bones of mammoth, woolly rhinoceros, reindeer, musk ox, arctic fox and hares. In the mountain regions flourished giant stag, stag, elk, ibex, bison, aurochs, cave bear, brown bear, wolf and fox. On the far-reaching forest steppes Man met mostly horses and oxen though often also carnivores such as cave-lion, cave-leopard and cave-hyena.

The cold forced men to wrap themselves in furs and so to make clothes. In the winter the Neanderthaloids lived in caves and grottoes, in the summer they changed over to open-air settlements near to water. Perhaps we also may set at this time the first beginnings of house-building. Caves and grottoes are known where the Neanderthaloids buttressed walls with stones and built up entrances. On the open-air sites they made complicated lodgings whose foundations consisted of the bones and skulls of big animals and whose roof was of brushwood over which were stretched skins. In some places mammoth skulls were stuck in the ground and their tusks served as rafters. One such lodging was found not long ago at Site Molodovo I on the middle reaches of the Dniester, while at the neighbouring Molodovo V are the remains of a row of less clearly defined shelters (excavations of S. Chernysh).

The roots of very primitive cults also seem to reach back into the Mousterian. The dead buried in the floors of caves are proof of this. Most of the skeletons discovered are in a quite definite and characteristic position with legs bent and drawn up against the body.

Some finds of purposely broken human bones in Mousterian levels point to traces of cannibalism. It is not improbable that the Neanderthaloids, especially in the great cold when hunting did not go too well, ate some of their fellow-men and perhaps also strangers or enemies.

It was in 1856 that not far from Düsseldorf in the Feldhofer cave of the Neanderthal were discovered the bones of an ancient type of Man. These consisted of the vault of the skull, both ulnae and the right radius, fragments of the right collar-bone and of the shoulder-blade, pieces of five ribs, of the pelvis and the bones of the upper part of the thigh.

A year later the anatomist Schaaffhausen made a first report on this discovery and drew the attention of scientists to the morphological peculiarities of the skeleton. The Neanderthal skull indeed offered a whole number of features which differentiated it strikingly from the skulls of recent Man. It was long and wide but also very low, the forehead small, the powerful supraorbital region formed a torus, the back of the head was flattened but markedly projecting.

Later on at various sites in Belgium, France, Spain, Italy and other countries of Europe, as well as in Asia and Africa, remains of early Man were discovered with similar characters and all these have been included in one anthropological class as 'Neanderthaloids' from the place of discovery of the first specimen (*Homo neanderthalensis*, King, 1864).

It is noteworthy that with the 'classical' Neanderthaloids sexual dimorphism seems to be more marked than in recent Man. Some skulls which seemed to show what looked like 'progressive' features proved to be, on thorough examination and study, those of females (e.g. Saccopastore I, Gibraltar I).

Most probably the Neanderthaloids lived in Europe from the Riss-Würm Interglacial to Würm glaciation I.

In our description of the reconstructions we shall endeavour, by basing it on the evidence of stratigraphy and cultures, to present, as far as possible, the specimens in chronological order.

The Saccopastore Woman

In 1929 during excavations in the deposits of the Anione stream not far from Rome the Italian anthropologist Sergio Sergi came across the fairly well-preserved skull of a woman. It lay in a level dating from the middle of the Riss-Würm Interglacial—and that indicates an age of about 100,000 years.

The skull possesses undoubtedly neanderthaloid features; the forehead, however, is rather more steep and the supraorbital region not so strongly marked as in many Neanderthaloids. The eye-sockets are round and high, the interorbital width moderate and the long nasal bones not very projecting. The pear-shaped nasal aperture was of shortened proportions and was comparatively small. The upper jaw and the cheek-bones, as far as they were preserved, were more delicate than usual in most Neanderthaloids. On account of these features Sergi thought the skull belonged to a special type of evolved Neanderthaloid with *sapiens* features.

For our reconstruction we had only at our disposal a drawing of the skull so that we had to limit ourselves to a pictorial reconstruction.

After the reconstruction was finished the head presented in its main characters that of a 'classical' Neanderthaloid and in my opinion did not show, as Sergi thought, a type developing towards *Homo sapiens* but rather one on the way to that specialisation which is so characteristic of the 'classical' Neanderthaloid. Moreover, the rather milder relief of this female skull is, we think, to be attributed rather to sexual dimorphism than to anything else.

The Le Moustier Youth

On the right bank of the Vezere river in the Dordogne department of France there is a small plateau with several terrace-like steps and numerous grottoes and caves. It was here that the flint industry was identified and defined by Gabriel de Mortillet as the 'Mousterian culture'.

In March 1908, O. Hauser came across the bones of a man in the lower grotto of Le Moustier. The skeleton was that of a youth about sixteen years of age and was cleaned by H. Klaatsch in the presence of a delegation from the Frankfurt Anthropological Congress.

Klaatsch was able to note that it was an intentional burial. The skeleton lay as though in an attitude of sleep, on its right side with arm and hand under the head while the left arm was stretched out along the body. Near the left hand were two fine early Mousterian artefacts, a point and a scraper. Under the skull and around the facial bones were a number of flint flakes and near the skeleton were animal bones which possibly may have had some ritual significance; this fauna dates the discovery to the early part of Würm I glaciation, and this is confirmed by the type of the Mousterian industry.[1]

In 1925, after many fruitless attempts, Weinert was able to restore the skull. The cranium was broad and low-vaulted, the forehead not high but relatively sheer. The back of the head was rounded. The temporal bones were small. There was no mastoid process. The eye-sockets were very high, the interorbital breadth fairly wide, the nasal bones only moderately projecting, the nasal aperture comparatively small and pear-shaped. The cheek-bones had the characteristic neanderthaloid slant above and below. The face was not broad, the alveolar area of the upper jaw, however, high, massive and with large teeth. The lower jaw had a thickened body, short, broad rami and no chin eminence. With so many details the skull of the Le Moustier youth came very near to the norm of the 'classical' Neanderthaloids, neverthe-

[1] Hauser's devastating excavations aroused much indignation in France which led to legislation protecting prehistoric sites. Hauser sold the skeleton for some 10,000 sovereigns to the Berlin museum where it was destroyed during the bombardments of the 1939–1945 war (translator's note).

less there were certain peculiarities of formation which could most readily be explained by the youth of the individual. Typical of the 'classical' Neanderthaloids are a massive supraorbital region particularly developed at the sides, great intraorbital width and a very prominent, broad nose. All these features are clearly marked in the later neanderthaloid skulls such as those of La Ferrassie, La Chapelle-aux-Saints and Monte Circeo. So the Le Moustier youth was apparently of an earlier type and lived probably about 70,000 years ago. The portrait we reconstructed from the skull gives a clear view of his appearance.

The La Quina Woman

In the years from 1910 to 1921 the French anthropologist Henri-Martin conducted excavations in one of the most revealing sites at the rock-shelter of La Quina. It contained several Mousterian levels and in several horizons he discovered about twenty disturbed burials. Most of them had been damaged in prehistoric times and therefore the bones were very badly preserved. Details of only two of the La Quina skulls have been published, one is that of an old woman and the other of a child about eight years old. Our interest was directed only to the female skull found by Henri-Martin on 18th September 1911. It was discovered *in situ* in a level of mid-Mousterian culture which can be dated to the first half of the Würm glaciation—or about 60,000 years ago.

In its general appearance this La Quina skull resembles that of Le Moustier and differs from the 'classical' Neanderthaloids mainly in its facial construction. The face indeed was higher, narrower and only slightly prognathous. The eye-sockets were high and of rounded contour, the nose was rather narrow and not very prominent while the cheek-bones were thinner.

The reconstructed head, however, showed most of the characteristics of the Neanderthaloids—a very low cranial vault, a coarse, long face and a retreating chin. We purposely did not reproduce the hair. Although the head was gross and ugly it did not present any specifically anthropoid features. With all its primitive traits it was a human face some of whose separate details are to be found even in *Homo recens*.

The La Ferrassie Neanderthaloid

The La Ferrassie site is in the French department of the Dordogne not far from the small town of Le Bugue. La Ferrassie consists of a complex of several levels of habitation sites belonging to various epochs of the Palaeolithic. The earliest of these dates from the latter part of the Acheulian when men settled under a rock-shelter. Later there lived here Neanderthaloids of the Mousterian who in the Aurignacian were replaced by *Homo sapiens*.

In 1909 the archaeologist Peyron discovered below the late Mousterian level the upper part of a hominid thigh-bone. A group of archaeologists and anthropologists (among them Capitan, Boule, Carthailhac, Breuil and Bouyssonie) freed a skeleton and studied it *in situ*. On this occasion the stratigraphical composition of the burial-place could be determined. The skeletal remains lay among an undisturbed cultural level at a depth of from 2 to 3 metres. The overlying level contained a late Mousterian industry which had accumulated during Man's lengthy settlement at the site. Together with traces of hearths innumerable animal bones were found and under this stratum remains of burials which clearly had been made at the very beginning of human settlement at the site. The first burial was that of a woman, the second that of a man and somewhat away from these were two children's graves. In all cases, these were undoubtedly intentional interments.

The associated fauna—reindeer, stag, horse and bison—indicated a cold, raw climate, that of the Würm glaciation about 50,000 years ago.

What interests us here is only the grave of the man. The skeleton lay on its back and slightly inclined to the left. The legs, once flexed at the knees, had fallen to the right side. The right arm was bent with the hand on a level with the face. The left arm lay stretched out along the body. The buried man had been strewn with a thin layer of earth and had certainly been covered with skins held in place with flat stones which lay over the bones of the skull and torso. The position of the skeleton and the circumstances of the burial led to the conclusion that this intentional interment must have taken place accompanied by the protection afforded by traditions that were already well developed.

The male skull of La Ferrassie is undoubtedly one of the best preserved among those of the European Neanderthaloids. To judge by the degree of wear of the teeth and of the obliteration of the sutures, the age of the man was about fifty years. In its morphological features the skull represents a typical Neanderthaloid of the late 'classical' variety. The vault was low, the forehead sloping, the region over the eyes was powerfully developed, the back of the head was flattened above and below but projected strongly. The small temporal bones showed a relatively slight mastoid process.

The large, massive face was very broad and had a markedly projecting nose. The eye-sockets were of typical neanderthaloid form but were not very high. Also the cheek-bones were typical. The profile of the face was marked and the alveolar region massive. The mandible showed certain progressive features, its body was not massive, the rami very thin, and it showed a trace of a projecting chin.

One anomaly was very noteworthy. The base of the skull was strongly displaced towards the left. This displacement was caused by no post-mortem deformation but was an individual feature in the living individual. The right condyle was compensatorily deformed so that the man of La Ferrassie suffered no loss of mobility of the head but carried it only slightly inclined towards the left.

Of this skeleton there remained besides the skull only fragments of the long bones and some other small pieces of bone. For our reconstruction the shoulder-blade was especially informative. From its construction the drooping shoulders of the Neanderthaloids could be more exactly copied and the degree of development of the muscles of the back better estimated, since the shoulder-blades of the Neanderthaloids were, morphologically speaking, rather sharply distinguished from those of *Homo sapiens*. The shoulder-blades of the former were rather larger and had a different contour. The powerful crests for the muscles of the nape, the position of the foramen magnum and the small mastoid processes, indicated the shape and degree of development of the main muscles of the neck and shoulders. To all appearances the muscles of the neck and back were very strong. But the muscle controlling the movements of the head and whose main function is to hold the head upright was relatively weak and not developed to the same extent as in *Homo sapiens,* though the weakness of this muscle was compensated for by the powerful development of the muscles at the back of the head and the neck.

So the Man of La Ferrassie displayed the whole complex of the classical Neanderthaloids' specific peculiarities. His height was about 150 centimetres (about 60 inches); he had a disproportionally large head, a massive, short neck and a stout, short torso. Arms and legs also were relatively short and the thighs and calves not fleshy but muscular. The feet had not very marked heels and therefore were somewhat turned inwards and so may have given the impression of a somewhat uncertain gait, but in reality the Neanderthaloid stood very firmly on his two legs, was mobile and nimble, he reacted with lightning rapidity and displayed a great elasticity in his coarse limbs. His small hand-worked artefacts and the high quality of his knapping technique make us conclude that he knew very well how to make excellent use of his coarse, thick, short-fingered hands.

The reconstructed head of the La Ferrassie Man agreed very well with our idea of what the highly specialised type of the developed Mousterian culture-phase was like.

The Neanderthaloid of La Chapelle-aux-Saints

In the year 1908 the archaeologists A. and J. Bouyssonie and L. Bardon discovered in the Bouffia cave not far from the village of La Chapelle-aux-Saints (Correze department of France) a man's skeleton. It lay in a grave cut down into the ground and under a completely undisturbed layer from 30 to 40 centimetres in thickness containing a number of artefacts of developed Mousterian type.

Clearly the man, who lived about 50,000 years ago, had been buried right at the beginning of this culture. The position of the skeleton in a depression in the rock-floor, the accompanying artefacts, the shells and remains of meals all indicated an intentional interment accompanied by a definite ritual. Near the skeleton lay the bones of a woolly rhinoceros, a horse, a reindeer and a bison. The fauna and the artefacts of the overlying stratum were characteristic of a late phase of developed Mousterian.

The La Chapelle-aux-Saints remains are among the best-preserved of European neanderthaloid discoveries and consist of an almost complete skull, all the vertebrae, ribs, fragments of the pelvis, the leg, hand and foot bones.

Marcellin Boule, the anthropologist, examined the bones thoroughly and described them at length. He set the man's age at between fifty-five and sixty and later even undertook a reconstruction of the main head muscles.

The skull, however, was not quite complete. A considerable portion of the parietal bones was missing and the nasal bones were broken off. As is indicated by the condition of the sockets the incisors of both jaws must have been lost after death. All the other teeth however must have dropped out a considerable time before death. This is indicated by the marked reduction in the size of the jaw. Only the left canines remained in place.

The La Chapelle-aux-Saints skull ranks as the type-specimen of the 'classical' European Neanderthaloids. The low skull vault was flattened and had a broad, well-modelled forehead with the typical projecting supraorbital region. The back of the head was wide, flattened above and below but strongly prominent with a marked occipital torus. The foramen magnum was situated somewhat backwards. The temporal bones were small and the mastoid process feebly developed.

The face was large, broad, orthognathous and the profile well marked. The priform nasal opening was very broad and large. The powerful nose must have jutted forwards. The eye-sockets were high and rounded in shape, the cheek-bones flattened. The alveolar region despite its shrinkage was still massive, and the lower jaw showed no specifically neanderthaloid features. There was no chin eminence and the rami were relatively short and broad.

The Gibraltar Woman

In 1848 Flint came across a hominid skull in a bone-filled breccia layer of a stone quarry behind Forbes's Battery on the north side of the rock of Gibraltar. Although this skull displayed primitive features, the discovery aroused no special interest. It was not until sixteen years after the discovery that the geologist G. Busk presented the specimen at a meeting of the British Association, and the skull began to be talked about. Some scientists saw in it the 'missing link' between recent Man and his ape-like ancestors.

The skull was that of a woman at least forty years old. The vault was much damaged. The remaining portions of the face were very massive. There was a marked supraorbital torus, a retreating chin, extraordinarily high and almost circular eye-sockets, a moderately powerful and projecting nose, a heavy upper jaw and the characteristic flattened cheek-bones. In a word the specimen was from the morphological point of view that of a typical Neanderthaloid of the 'classical' sort.

Many researchers, however, have wanted to see in it features of an advanced type and have compared it with the Saccopastore skull. Moreover, it has been advanced that this skull, owing to its specific traits, represents a milestone on the evolutionary road towards *Homo sapiens*.

Effectively the skull vault of the Gibraltar fossil was shorter and higher, the forehead steeper, the whole relief slighter, the face lower, the eye-sockets rounder and higher, the foramen magnum more centred—but all these features do not exceed those due to sexual dimorphism among the Neanderthaloids, or in fact those which distinguish female from male skulls among *Homo sapiens* where the former, as a rule, have shorter proportions of the vault, a smoother relief and higher eye-orbits.

The Monte Circeo Man

In 1939 the late A. C. Blanc, the Italian geologist and archaeologist, found a skull in a cave of the Monte Circeo (some sixty-five miles southwards from Rome). The objects associated with the find were, however, so unusual that suspicions were aroused that the discovery might be a case of forgery. All doubts were, however, set at rest by a number of pieces of evidence—the degree of mineralisation of the skull-bones, the calcareous accretions and, most important of all, the morphological peculiarities of the specimen.

The circumstances of the discovery were these: Blane came across in the middle of a small cave a depression in the stone which to all appearances indicated the emplacement of an ancient hearth. In this fireplace lay a skull. It was considerably damaged although the mutilation was clearly inflicted before death. The right cheek-bone, the adjoining part of the frontal and the upper part of the parietal were smashed and it would seem not by a blow on the head but on the skull when it had already been scalped. All the teeth (some of whose roots were still in their sockets) had been knocked out and the base of the skull destroyed. The state of the skull, therefore, gave the impression that the damage had been done with the object of removing the brain.

In the cave was also found the portion of a lower jaw which, however, was so uncharacteristic that its provenance could not be determined. No other hominid bones were discovered at the Monte Circeo site.

After a thorough examination of all the facts in the case Professor Sergio Sergi came to the conclusion that the state of the skull and its position indicated ritual cannibalism. Obviously the man must have been eaten outside the cave and his skull then disposed, to the accompaniment of some ritual unknown to us, in the cave.

Later Mousterian burials indicate that not only did Neanderthaloids care for their dead fellow-men but that interment was linked with a definite ritual.

At some sites traces of cannibalism have been found—such as at Krapina rock-shelter where remains of bones and skulls were found among kitchen refuse. And there are other indications that the Neanderthaloids already possessed quite complicated associations of ideas. Their spiritual degree of evolution must not then be underestimated. They were men with their own perceptions of the world in which they lived however different these may have been from ours.

Clearly the Monte Circeo man belonged to the 'classical' type and displayed all its specific characteristics.

The reconstruction showed a massive head with very low retreating forehead, much developed supraorbital region, a broad, thick and rather shapeless nose. The small, close-set eyes appeared to be hidden under the shelter of the torus over them.

The whole appearance was one of primitiveness. What emerged from our hands was a man but at the same time a creature with animal-like craft and cunning.

The geological and stratigraphical evidence of Monte Circeo points to a dating towards the end of the second half of Würmian glaciation I. And this fits in well with the morphological peculiarities of the skull.

The Boy in the Teshik-Tash Grotto

In the mountain valley of the Shirabad-Darya river south of Samarkand and west of Baisun, A. P. Okladnikov discovered, on investigating the Baisun-Tau, a Mousterian site comprising several strata in the Tashik-Tash grotto.

The artefacts in all five culture horizons belong to a phase which much resembled the Levalloisian-Mousterian of western and central Asia as well as of Palestine. The principal quarry of the Teshik-Tash men was the Siberian ibex (*Capra sibirica*).

In 1938 Okladnikov, while clearing the top cultural level, came upon a burial at a depth of about 25 centimetres (about 10 inches). The skull was broken into more than 150 pieces, which, however, individually were in good condition. Besides the skull there were found also portions of the skeletal bones—an atlas, several ribs, a bone of the upper arm, an upper thigh bones and phalanges.

We were able to restore the skull and fit it together into an almost complete whole. It had undoubtedly belonged to a child of about nine or ten years of age, but it was considerably larger and heavier than that of a 'modern' child of the same age and this was especially true as regards the dimensions of the facial bones.

The skull-vault was relatively low, the muscular relief remarkably strongly developed. The retreating forehead and the supraorbital area were in size and shape typically neanderthaloid. The upper jaw and the cheek-bones were very massive, the nose was only slightly projecting yet the piriform nasal opening was very big. The alveolar portion was also massive. The primitive lower jaw was typical, had no chin eminence but possessed a thickened body and a broad, short ramus. Although the skeleton was that of an immature person it displayed a collection of features which obviously resembled those of the Neanderthaloids of the late Mousterian in Europe.

G. F. Debez is of the opinion that sequence of the teeth eruption in this skull did not quite correspond to the norm in recent Man and concluded that the child was at the most nine years of age. The whole dimensions and measurements of the skull, the degree of development of the muscular relief, the size of the remaining teeth and a number of other features justify the supposition that the skull was that of a male.

We made several attempts to reconstruct the head and face of this child from the Teshik-Tash grotto and in doing this were careful to present an as authentic as possible reproduction of his outward appearance.

We do not consider the hypothesis sufficiently proved that the skull presents features of a 'progressive' type, i.e. resembling *Homo sapiens*. It should perhaps be borne in mind that it is the skull of a child so that, for instance, the comparatively high vault and the not very pronounced development of the region over the eyes should be taken rather as marks of immaturity and not as 'progressive' features.

The Teshik-Tash artefacts bore a great resemblance to the industry in the Levalloisian level at the Tabun grotto in Palestine, where the skeleton of a female was discovered. It is not impossible that the Teshik-Tash boy and the Tabun woman were more or less contemporaries. If this was the case then the former would have lived at the end of the Mousterian—that is to say before 40,000 years ago.

The Mousterian Men of Palestine

In 1925 the series of fruitful excavations in Palestinian cave-sites began which provided a mass of archaeological and palaeo-anthropological evidence. During the years 1931–2 the archaeologist D. A. E. Garrod and the anthropologist McCown undertook the exploration of the Mount Carmel caves—the Tabun and the Es-Skhul. In both caverns were found at about the same cultural horizon, altogether eleven interments of Mousterian Man. We could, however, produce only three reconstructions.

The Woman of Tabun I

The Tabun grotto first occupied in Acheulian times was, during the course of millenia, constantly inhabited. The total depth of the cultural layers was as much as 15·5 metres (over 60 feet): the transition from late Acheulian to Levalloisian was clearly marked. In the upper cultural level (horizon C) the remains of a woman were discovered. The artefacts of this level consisted of a peculiar mixture of Levalloisian and Mousterian. Besides small points and scrapers there were also faceted cores and knives.

The stratigraphy, the nature of the surrounding stratum and especially the position of the skeleton indicates an intentional burial. The skeleton lay on its back with outstretched legs but the left arm was bent at right angles and the hand turned towards the left. The burial was orientated towards the west. In the grave neither artefacts nor animal bones were to be found. The skeletal remains were in a very bad condition.

The woman was about 151 centimetres (some 60 inches) tall, the bones were thin and delicate. The skull could be removed and restored. At a first glance it gave an impression of being very primitive and appeared from its general shape to be nearly related to the 'classical' Neanderthaloids. But on closer inspection the resemblance did not seem to be so great and it was due mostly to the strongly developed supraorbital region and the lack of a chin.

A careful examination convinced us, indeed, that the skull differed considerably from the female skulls of typical European Neanderthaloids—such as those of Saccopastore, La Quina and even Gibraltar I. The Tabun I skull was certainly dolichocephalic but of another shape, the vault was relatively speaking wider and loftier, the forehead less retreating, the glabella projected less than the middle of the supraorbital 'bulge' or torus. This feature was more like that of a Sinanthropus than a classical Neanderthaloid. The back of the head was rounded, the foramen magnum was placed farther forward and the temporal bones were higher. In these traits the Tabun I skull did show a tendency towards *Homo sapiens* forms.

The face also possessed quite different morphological foundations (from those of classical Neanderthaloids)—it was less massive, not so strongly profiled and it was orthognathous. The broad nose did not jut out so markedly. The shape of the cheek-bones more resembled that of the Cro-Magnon type than that of the Neanderthaloids.

The reconstructed head was set upright on the neck. The face showed, with all its pronounced ugliness and certain primitive characteristics, clearly recognisable features of *Homo sapiens* and this impression was not lessened either by the markedly projecting over-eye region, the amorphous form of the nose or the retreating chin region.

So the Tabun I woman on the grounds of morphology alone might be regarded as a transitional type in the direction of recent Man—if she had not lived so late. According to the most recent researches her absolute age may be fixed at 41,000 years. At that time however there existed already not only in Europe but in other places men of *Homo sapiens* type. Possibly therefore the Tabun I woman may pass as a hybrid between late Neanderthaloid Man and progressive *Homo sapiens*.

The Mousterian Man from Es-Skhul grotto

A little over 200 yards from the Tabun grotto is the Es-Skhul cave in which Dr. Garrod and McCown discovered a number of burials dating from a late phase of the Levalloisian-Mousterian culture. Es-Skhul was occupied by Man a very considerable time after Tabun. In the former the palaeolithic cultural horizons reached a depth of 2·5 metres (about 8 feet). The topmost level (A) contained artefacts of Aurignacian, that is to say Upper Palaeolithic, culture. It is noteworthy that this level showed a connection with the level below (B) which presented implements of late Levalloisian-Mousterian type. Still deeper down was a stratum with artefacts of an earlier phase of Levalloisian.

In levels B and B1 and at different depths altogether, nine interments of Mousterian Man were unearthed. We are interested here only in the fourth and the fifth since from the specimens in question, portraits of these long-dead men could be reconstructed.

Both burials were found in the upper part of B1 level and were obviously to be dated to a time when B level was being formed and therefore must be attributed to more or less the same cultural phase which was also that of the Tabun I female skeleton.

The artefacts from level C of the Tabun grotto and those from the B level of the Es-Skhul cave are, generally speaking, related, though not absolutely identical. The implements from B level seem to be the more evolved.

The remains from Es-Skhul burial 4 were the best preserved. The skeleton lay on its side with legs flexed at the knees, the arms were bent at the elbows and the hands were before the face.

The bones from burial Es-Skhul 5 were in a worse condition; however, it could be determined that the dead man had been laid on his back; arms and legs were also flexed. On the breast lay the lower jaw of a wild boar; McCown supposed that this must have been placed in the hands of the corpse.

The skull of Es-Skhul 4 was markedly different from that of a Neanderthaloid, the vault was higher, the back of the head not so much flattened, the forehead higher, the supraorbital region powerfully developed but not of typically neanderthaloid form but rather showed a resemblance to that of *Homo sapiens*. The face was relatively short, the eye-sockets were low and lengthened and therefore different from those of the Neanderthaloids. The nose must have projected sharply but was not so broad.

Also the alveolar region was otherwise formed. The cheek-bones were of *sapiens* type. The heavy lower jaw had a clearly marked chin. In its general appearance the skull reminded one of an archaic europoid type.

The skeletal bones also showed some resemblance to those of *Homo sapiens*. The upper part of the thigh was straight, the proportions of the leg, that is to say the relation of the length of the upper part of the thigh to that of the lower, corresponded to that of the earliest types of *Homo sapiens* and in this the man of Es-Skhul 4 differed strikingly from the Neanderthaloids. Of all the skeletons discovered in Palestine this was the one in which *sapiens* character was most markedly shown.

But according to our opinion the skull of the Mousterian Man of Es-Skhul 5 showed no Neanderthaloid features at all. It had a strong relief and resembled from many points of view a recent

Australoid skull. The vault was rather high but the forehead retreating and the supraorbital region powerfully modelled, the face was prognathous, the nose wide but not very prominent, the chin was clearly indicated but not projecting. The eye-sockets were low and wide and thus had quite other proportions from those of the Neanderthaloids. The cheek-bones in their shape approximated to those of contemporary Man.

It could be said, indeed, that taken as a whole all the skeletons from the Tabun and Es-Skhul caves displayed strongly marked features both of the Neanderthaloids and of recent Man. From this many authorities have concluded these Mousterian men represented a transition stage from the Neanderthaloids to the evolved form of recent Man. But this view does not seem to be justified. We would point out that the Mousterian men of Palestine lived at a time when, in neighbouring regions, recent Man already existed.

The Mousterian Child of Staroselie

In 1952 the archaeologist A. A. Formosov discovered a late Mousterian site at a place called Staroselie near Bakehiserai in the Crimea. The site was cleared in the presence of a special commission composed of professors S. M. Samiatnin, Y. Y. Roginski and M. M. Gerasimov who determined the circumstances of the discovery and removed the remains in a block (together with the earth saturated with an adhesive mixture) so that a reconstruction of the skull was possible.

The child was intentionally interred almost on the very edge of the site, under the rock-roof and away from the living-floor. Before the burial the grave was carefully prepared, cleared of stones and levelled. The skeleton lay, with outstretched legs, on its back, the arms rather bent at the elbows and the hands placed together on the torso. There were no other objects present. It is, however, quite possible that the child's body was covered with a hide which was then strewn with a thin layer of earth.

Some time, probably quite soon, after the burial, part of the rock-roof had become detached and buried the interment under a layer of stone. With time the living-site was enlarged and extended over the grave, so as to form a cultural stratum of a considerable size, containing many animal bones, flint flakes and other artefacts.

The child's age could be estimated at from one and a half to two years. The morphological features of the skull showed that the child represented an intermediate form between the late Neanderthaloid and the early *Homo sapiens*.

Among the primitive features must be reckoned the massive lateral portion of the supraorbital region, the remarkable size of the teeth, the peculiar form of the lower jaw's alveolar arch, the very slightly projecting chin, the rather small temporal bones and the only slightly marked mastoid process. On the other hand, the high vault of the skull, the steep forehead and the construction of the facial skeleton displayed fully developed features of a very early *Homo sapiens*.

The external shape of the skull came very near to those of the Grimaldi youth and the Man of Markina Gora. All these skulls show, in addition to primitive features and some of those of recent Man, quite unmistakable peculiarities belonging to the anthropological equatorial type.

Rhodesian Man

In 1921 at a lead and zinc mine near the railway station of Broken Hill in Northern Rhodesia (now Zambia) there were discovered by chance the bones of a man.

On the western slopes of a hill, almost at its foot was a deep 'bone-bearing' cave half-filled with the remains of various animals —elephant, rhinoceros, antelope, lion and leopard. In the deepest part of the cavern and above a mass of animal bones, a human skull was found. Nearby lay fragments of the skeletal bones together with portions of the upper jaw of another man.

The dating of the Broken Hill skull has not yet been quite satisfactorily estimated. The problem has been tackled by the scientists Clark, Wells, O'Clay and McClellan. Their general conclusion has been that the discovery belongs to a relatively late period. This opinion is supported also by the very evolved artefacts found near the skull. These were made up of cores, flakes, scrapers, points and a bone splinter which shows traces of having been worked. L. H. Wells (in 1950) attributed these to the Proto-Stillbay southern African cultural complex, and the skull itself was dated to the beginning of the upper Gamblian phase. The cranium is very massive with a projecting supraorbital torus, a flattened forehead and a projecting occipital region. The protuberances of the occipital area and the crests at the nape of the neck were strongly developed. The foramen magnum and the mastoid process resembled in form those in recent Man. The face was large and massive, the eye-sockets very large and high, the nose broad and only slightly projecting, the cheek-bones heavy, the upper jaw high, coarse and most primitive.

The teeth were much worn down, had low crowns and many of them were decayed. Rhodesian Man possessed a powerful torso and long straight legs. The strongly developed regions for the attachment of muscles denoted extraordinary bodily power.

The peculiar combination of very primitive traits with those of a progressive type offers a morphological curiosity, and there is up to now no clear indication as to the place Rhodesian Man occupies in the general process of the evolution of recent Man.

The Upper Palaeolithic and Homo sapiens fossilis

At the beginning of the Upper Palaeolithic the Neanderthaloids were replaced by a new hominid form—the so-called *Homo sapiens*.

The climate of the Upper Palaeolithic, particularly in Europe, was at first cold and dry, but with the retreat of the glaciers became damper and towards the end of the period approximated to that of today. Therefore the cold-loving animals moved gradually northwards. Towards the end of the Upper Palaeolithic the woolly rhinoceros and the mammoth died out while the reindeer retreated to the north as did also the musk-ox. However, the climatic change did not occur everywhere in the same degree. If the glaciation constantly decreased, the changes were swayed to and fro without any perceptible general pattern.

The climatic variations must of course have influenced early Man. His whole manner of life which was linked mainly with hunting was altered. Now he must often follow the animal herds. Towards the end of the Palaeolithic the change in the fauna necessitated new hunting techniques and here and there even to a predominance of a gathering economy. We may set the beginning of the Upper Palaeolithic to a date of between 60,000 and 40,000 years ago and its end to 10,000 years ago at the least. The whole of the Upper Palaeolithic was dominated by 'recent Man' or *Homo sapiens* and during the first part of the epoch occurred the development of the fundamental characteristics of the various races.

We think it very important that the reader should be able to form a right idea as to what we understand by the concept of 'Human Races'. They are essentially formed by men in a definite area, men of the same origin and possessing in common a number of morphological features whose variability is determined by the characteristic traits of this or that group. These historically developed communities of men of one type are called 'races'.

Such an historical definition of 'race' allows us to recognise their further differentiation at various formative periods. The whole of the present-day population of the earth consists of one kind of Man —*Homo sapiens*.

The more recently discovered remains of very ancient Man and what we know now of the area of his settlements allow us to set the probable limits of the areas where the early forms of present-day Man developed.

It seems, however, to be firmly established that the specialised Neanderthaloid groups played no part in the development of present-day Man. They kept their appearance and their culture and lived their conservative lives for a time as contemporaries of the early representatives of the developing *Homo sapiens*. It goes without saying that the new human type could not have developed everywhere at the same rate. The pace was probably determined above all by the relations between the various human groups in the area. The new social contacts, especially about the middle of the Mousterian, the appearance of differentiation, articulate language and the level of material culture all led to greater communication between the various human groups. Thus arose a new pace of evolution and a new norm of sexual relations which can count as the main causes of the development of modern Man.

Clearly in the earlier phases of *Homo sapiens* evolution he must in some measure have possessed latently the 'elements' so to speak of the main human races, but these only later found their exteriorisation.

The process of race-formation was determined to a certain extent by the pace of Man's settlement beyond the areas of his origin. Owing to his insufficiently stable biological constitution and lack of specialised forms, the Neanthropus must have had all sorts of possibilities open to him.

The very few remains from the time of the transition from Mousterian to Aurignacian respectively to the Szelettian cannot yet provide proof because of the lack of a connection between these cultures. The substitution of Aurignacian culture for Mousterian is no indication of the appearance of a new form of Man in another area.

Local varieties of Mousterian culture are certainly to be found and the differences they display are not so very great. They occur in almost all the areas of the Old World. On the other hand, the Upper Palaeolithic cultures are divided, quite unmistakably, into definite archaeological territorial provinces with specific, local forms of artefacts. The different forms appear so obviously that they serve as additional proof for the polycentric origin of the races among recent Man.

As the settlement areas of Neanthropus spread, all the new racial features were inherited by the only slightly differentiated Upper Palaeolithic Man by adaption and mingling with the original inhabitants.

Contemporaneously with the Upper Palaeolithic races there were formed local culture-provinces. At the present day six of these can be recognised.

1 The European Ice Age province.
2 The Mediterranean-Capsian province.
3 The Southern African province.
4 The Indo-Himalayan province.
5 The Siberian-Mongolian province.
6 The Malayan province.

In some of the above there are areas which certainly display one and the same development of industries but which none the less cannot be included in the uniform scheme. So, for instance, the European Ice Age province must be subdivided into a western and an eastern, the Mediterranean into a number of local sub-provinces. In south-western Asia and in Hindustan we meet with Capsian-like cultures. But there are also in the same province many large Mousterian-type artefacts of flint. It may be that here the influence of the Siberian-Mongolian province makes itself felt, some of whose sites are spread over the eastern slopes of the Pamir.

The portraits of Upper Palaeolithic Man in this book come mostly from the European Ice Age zone. Therefore we must content ourselves with the traditional cultural classification—Aurignacian, Solutrean and Magdalenian, although we do not consider them sufficiently complete.

The Aurignacian and Related Culture Phases

After a very thorough research campaign undertaken into the stratigraphy of a number of sites with several levels, the archaeologists Breuil and Cartailhac were able to detect Aurignacian culture at Aurignac, La Ferrassie, Pair-non-Pair (Gironde), in the Abri-Audit grotto, at La Cotte, Spy and La Bouffia (Correze). In these places the archaeologists were able to detect, between the late Mousterian levels and the early Solutrean, a different culture with its own typical artefacts, a peculiar technique for the preparation of blades, and in addition an archaic kind of bone industry.

The early phase of the classical Aurignacian is distinguished indeed from the later Gravettian culture, so that it is a question whether the two are or are not linked. But the similar technical tradition and the typology of the artefacts leads us however to the conclusion that the Aurignacian and Gravettian cultures of southern Europe and north Africa must have evolved in one uniform line.

The widespread influence of these cultures was manifested in the uncommonly complicated forms of the local development in the Palaeolithic industries of the eastern part of the European 'diluvial' province. In the Black Earth zone of the Soviet Union, for example, at the Kostienki-Borshevski sites, on the Don, the local Aurignacian-type industry overlies the most evolved Solutrean, while in the western part of this province the Aurignacian precedes the Solutrean.

The classical Aurignacian culture is one of a highly developed art (engravings, paintings, drawings, sculpture) represented by many examples of a primitive-realistic style.

The area of the Mediterranean province (with Capsian and Gravettian cultures) is characterised by a quite surprising tradition of schematic rock-paintings which cannot be classed with the style of primitive realism. This is in the early phases of Upper Palaeolithic art especially associated with the Ice Age zone of Europe. Not so long ago a stalactitic cave on the southern slopes of the Urals was discovered. It contained polychrome Old Stone Age pictures—a rhinoceros, a mammoth and horses. Still more surprising is it that a similar form of primitive-realistic art is to be found in early Palaeolithic sites of eastern Siberia where not only figurines of women, birds and a bear but also drawings of mammoth and snakes and many ornamented implements and objects of adornment have been discovered (Mal'ta and Buret sites).

In type—and probably also in its dating—the Mal'ta culture comes close to the Aurignacian of Europe, but, nevertheless, the former is a culture of its own whose origin is, as yet, not clear. One thing only is certain, that it cannot be any European culture since its authors were early Mongoloids.

The artefacts of that period, both from the materials used and from the methods employed in knapping, are peculiar to the Mal'ta culture and indicate a certain specialisation, that is to say, the existence of some men apart from the mass of their fellows who possessed more ability and dexterity in the preparation of complicated hunting weapons, domestic utensils and works of art. Thanks to the mastery of technical novelties and their appropriate utilisation hunting methods became certainly more reasonable. Fishing, which in the economy of very early communities was not of great importance, in certain regions developed from a casual and auxiliary means of livelihood into a regular occupation.

Man built for himself complicated subterranean dwellings and earth-huts. He lived also in grottoes. He made the earliest sewn clothing and probably also primitive shoes. And in this period began no doubt the differentiation of work as between men and women. There appeared increasingly elaborate norms of sexual relations and family organisation. At the same time most ancient beliefs and magical rites make their appearance as did also the first methodical ritual burials.

Today the Aurignacian culture is no longer regarded as a uniform phase. From it derived the Perigordian culture, an early Aurignacian peculiar to France. The mid-Aurignacian retained its characteristics whereas the late-Aurignacian in a number of provinces developed into what is known as Gravettian. In various regions the Gravettian appears with specific local artefacts.

In western Europe the Mousterian is often replaced by the Aurignacian in a way that allows for elements of the transition from one culture to the other to be recognised. This is probably due to the fact that parts of Europe were included in the area where the recent type of Man became differentiated. We should not, however, conclude that the early forms of this kind of Man possessed the definite features of existing races. All known fossil skulls from the Aurignacian are in a high degree 'neutral' though diverse and can only from a few features be classed as Negroid, Australoid or Europoid. On account of these features the following various anthropological types can be distinguished:

1 Grimaldi: the oldest types of recent Man with features of both proto-Negroid and of Cro-Magnon Man.
2 Combe-Capelle: a not very differentiated type of recent Man but still with features of both proto-Europoid and proto-Australoid.
3 Cro-Magnon: the oldest Europoid type.

The Grimaldi Negroids

In 1901 the French archaeologist L. de Villeneuve found an Upper Palaeolithic burial in the Grotte des Enfants just over the Franco-Italian frontier beyond Menton. The grave contained the remains of a youth and a middle-aged woman. The position of the legs indicated an intentional interment and both bodies lay in the ashes of a large hearth. The lad lay on his back, the feet drawn up against the pelvis, the arms were stretched out along the body. The woman lay in a constricted position and covering the skeleton of the youth. Arms and legs were pressed closely to the chest. The youth had a filet of pierced sea-shells on his head and on his left arm two bracelets of the same ornaments, one at the elbow and the other on the wrist. The heads of the two skeletons were covered by a large slab of stone that rested on two upright supports. The grave was under an undisturbed Aurignacian level with Cro-Magnon-type skeletons. Under the grave was a Mousterian level.

Both skulls belonged to the same anthropological type and looked very much alike, both had high-vaulted, dolichocephalic crania, low, relatively broad faces, low eye-sockets and very broad, only slightly projecting noses. The upper jaws were prognathous, the lower jaws heavy, with broad rami and only feebly marked chin.

Both individuals were of low stature. The youth measured 150 centimetres (about 60 inches) and the woman some 155 centimetres. In the shape of the pelvis and the proportions of the legs Negroid and archaic features could be recognised (long upper arm and curved upper thigh). Both skulls displayed Negroid together with some Cro-Magnon features. From these skulls we prepared portrait-drawings which give an idea of *Homo sapiens* in the earlier part of the Upper Palaeolithic, that is to say at the beginning of Würm glaciation II and can be dated to between 40,000 and 30,000 years ago.

The Negroid of Markina Gora

In 1954 the archaeologist A. N. Rogatshov discovered a burial while he was excavating the several strata of the Markina Gora site. It lies on the middle reaches of the Don river not far from the village of Kostienki in the Voronezh region of the U.S.S.R.

The third culture horizon was undisturbed in its upper part but the lower part had been disturbed and had sunk in places. Thus the grave had been filled in from above. But the outline was clearly distinguishable. It was formed by a depression cut into the clayey soil with particles of volcanic ashes at the base.

The interment had taken place right at the beginning of the

third culture horizon in which horse bones and fragments of rose-white arenaceous quartz predominated but there were some split black flints. The scrapers, chisels, the artefacts with retouched edges and fragments of bone hafts indicated that the burial took place though not in the beginning of the Upper Palaeolithic, still at an early period. The Markina Gora remains must date from somewhat later than those of Grimaldi. The removal, the cleaning and the preservation of the bones were undertaken by my daughter Magarita and I.

The buried man lay in a low, narrow grave, oval in shape and with almost upright walls. The skeleton like those of the Grimaldi Negroids was tightly bent together. The position indicated that the corpse must have been bound round before burial. The bones were plentifully strewn with red ochre and there were no artefacts present.

The Markina Gora Man showed no Neanderthaloid characteristics. He was rather a perfect type of recent Man with, however, specific features of a fossil Negroid. In the shape of the long bones, nevertheless, he displayed certain primitive features from which it may be concluded that in walking he always held his knees slightly flexed and the feet turned inwards.

Although the Markina Gora Man showed a whole complex of Negroid features, he was not like the existing Negroes. He possessed indeed all the features peculiar to the Neanthropi of the early Upper Palaeolithic. But in general appearance he was undoubtedly very much like the Grimaldi Negroids, and resembled most the Papuans among existing races—the same large forehead, long cranium, strongly projecting, wide nose, general facial prognathism, slightly protruding lips and poorly developed chin.

Combe-Capelle Man

In 1909 Otto Hauser recovered a well preserved skeleton in the Combe-Capelle rock-shelter not far from Montferrand in the Perigord (France). It lay in an undisturbed Aurignacian level on its back with legs close together. The head and shoulders were covered with stone slabs. In the grave were stone artefacts and pierced sea-shells. The undisturbed level over the grave pointed to the conclusion that the interment took place at the beginning of the layer's formation. The implements in the grave corresponded with those typical of the early Aurignacian.

This phase of the French Upper Palaeolithic cultures is now called the 'Perigordian' and the Combe-Capelle grotto is classed as the type-site of this culture.

The Combe-Capelle Man was about 167 centimetres tall and possessed well-developed muscles. The skull showed the characteristics of *Homo sapiens fossilis* and features of both proto-Europoid and proto-Australoid types. On these gounds the anthropologist H. Klaatsch considered himself justified in classing the Combe-Capelle specimen as a distinct primitive race which he called *Homo sapiens aurignaciensis*. Its specific characteristics appeared clearly in the reconstruction.

Cro-Magnon Man

In the year 1875 during the construction of a railway-line in the valley of the Vezere, a grotto was discovered at a spot called Cro-Magnon close to the village of Les Eyzies. In the cave were found five skeletons as well as Aurignacian-type artefacts and objects of adornment. Three of the skeletons were of men, one was of a woman and one of a child. The morphological peculiarities of the skeletons were such that these could be classed together as a single type of *Homo sapiens fossilis*—Cro-Magnon Man. In south-western Europe Aurignacian culture is associated mostly with the Cro-Magnons. The first time a discovery of this sort was made was in Great Britain in 1823 when a skeleton without a skull but with Aurignacian artefacts was found in the Paviland Cave (Wales). The remains showed traces of red pigment and in anthropological literature the specimen is known as the 'Red Lady of Paviland' (though the bones are those of a youth and not a woman).

In 1852 in the Aurignac cave (in the foothills of the Pyrenees)—Haute-Garonne department—at least seventeen Cro-Magnon skeletons were discovered, while in the years from 1872 to 1901 in Aurignacian levels many burials were found in the Grimaldi caves near the Franco-Italian frontier on the Riviera (see p. 103). In the upper levels of the Grotte des Enfants there were four skeletons, in the Grotte de Cavillon one, in the Barma Grande six and in the Baousso da Torre grotto three.

The most striking feature of the Cro-Magnon skull is a disharmony between the narrow cranium and the broad, short face. Generally Cro-Magnon men have steep foreheads, only a slightly developed supraorbital region, low and wide eye-sockets, a strongly projecting, narrow nose, massive and flattened cheekbones and a slight alveolar prognathism of the heavy lower jaw.

Very high stature was characteristic of the early Cro-Magnon men. The Cavillon specimen measured 179 centimetres, Cro-Magnon (I) 182 centimetres, Barma Grande (II) 182 centimetres, Baoussa da Torre 185 centimetres, Barma Grande (I) 193 centimetres and the remains in Grotte des Enfants 194 centimetres, or 6 feet 4½ inches.

The muscle-relief of the Cro-Magnon skeleton was strongly developed; unlike modern Europeans, Cro-Magnon men had very long upper arms, compared with the shoulder and the lower part of the leg, long compared with the upper part. These limb proportions suggest those of the Negroids and it is noteworthy that the Cro-Magnon skull does show some slight indication of Negroid elements.

A specific peculiarity of the Cro-Magnon skeleton was the shape of the shank, markedly flattened at the sides but broad and sabre-shaped. Generally this form is associated with a high degree of development of the heel-bones. The long shank and massive heel-bones were combined with strong calf muscles. The upper thigh was, despite its comparative shortness, straight and strong. The high, broad and flattened pelvis with large hip bones indicates strong muscles of the upper thigh.

The legs were long, thin but muscular, the shoulder-bones comparatively short. Cro-Magnon Man had a powerful torso, broad shoulders and a high breast with narrow pelvis. Thus in their build and in the special conditions of the Upper Palaeolithic, they were better suited for hunting than any other type of Man since this demanded extensive and rapid changes of area as well as running and great muscular exertion.

So the Cro-Magnon Man was strong; he was also in his way good-looking. His type lasted for several thousand years and spread widely over the whole of the Old World. In Africa the Cro-Magnons gave rise to hybrids with Negroid traits and in Asia to types with Mongoloid features.

We made a considerable number of reconstructions which present Cro-Magnon Man's appearance at different times and in various regions. The most impressive is the reconstitution from Cro-Magnon skull I which dates from the middle Aurignacian phase and may be placed in Würm glaciation II (from about 30,000 to 20,000 years ago).

The Solutrean

In the western part of the European glaciation zone the Aurignacian culture is succeeded by the Solutrean. The changeover in culture can be observed in many French sites where there is a succession of cultural layers—as, for instance, at Aurignac, Brassempouy, La Ferrassie, Sulutré and Abri-Audit.

Quite often transitional phases can be found which show the development of new knapping techniques and hitherto unknown forms of artefacts.

Together with the traditional Aurignacian techniques in the early stages of the Solutrean are pressure-flaked tools, so that the preparation of artefacts with fine blades, javelin heads, daggers, knives and so forth, was possible. All the implements of the Solutrean are characterised by beautiful and perfect shapes.

In addition to the stone implements a bone industry developed —needles, blades, and daggers. Also art underwent an extensive development. Solutrean Man carved objects out of stone, mammoth tusks, deer horn, soft stone and of course wood. He also modelled not in clay alone but in a prepared mixture of clay, pounded bone, vegetable fibres, hair and feathers, compounded together it would seem, with animal fat.

Masterpieces of Solutrean art are known from France, Germany, Czechoslovakia and the Soviet Union. In Solutrean times men settled mostly in river valleys or in the open country and built themselves huts and shelters for larger communities on level ground.

In 1871 at Brüx in Bohemia a skull was discovered; in 1891 at

Brünn in Moravia, a human skeleton was found with mammoth remains, while in 1894 there were unearthed at Předmost (Moravia) the bones of eighteen individuals at a burial site together with human remains from individual graves. The Předmost, Brüx and Brünn skulls are mostly referred to as the Brünn-Předmost variety of the Cro-Magnon race. They differed from the typical Cro-Magnon skulls in that they were more delicate, had lower vaults, more retreating foreheads and a definitely more strongly developed supraorbital area. The eye-sockets are almost as low but the cheek-bones thinner and more prominent. The nose was not very projecting and the alveolar region is slightly prognathous. The lower jaw is less massive and has a high but flattened body and a not very marked chin.

The men of the Brünn-Předmost race were rather shorter than the Cro-Magnons, more slender and not so strongly built. The Brünn-Předmost skeletons show *sapiens* features combined with primitive traits so that their skulls have an archaic appearance. This type should, from the morphological point of view, occupy a place between *Homo sapiens* and the Neanderthaloids. But since they lived in later times than the Cro-Magnons it may be concluded that they occupy an exceptional place in the evolution of recent races. It seems possible that the Brünn-Předmost type may have arisen from a fusion of Cro-Magnon Man and a group of Neanderthaloids. Thus perhaps were due certain primitive features which are not found in the classical Cro-Magnons.

The Magdalenian

The Magdalenian culture of the European Pleistocene followed on the Solutrean in the last phase of the Ice Age. The beginning of this period was marked by a cold, damp climate much like that of the tundra today. But the later stages of this period were characterised by notable climatic changes. The weather became colder and drier, the steppe landscape spread northwards and occupied the place of the tundra marshes . . . mammoths died out and the reindeer moved on to the high ground and northwards. The typical fauna of central Europe resembled that of the steppes today—with the djiggetai horse and the saiga antelope.

Once more men sought shelter in caves and grottoes. In this period the Palaeolithic polychrome cave-paintings reached a high level. The caves of Altamira, Lascaux and many others have preserved marvellous pictures by prehistoric artists. Most of the representations are of animals and in their delineation and the skill with which the Old Stone Age artists managed to produce a plastic impression by the use of colour and the utilisation of rock contours, the cave-paintings are most impressive.

The Magdalenian age was also one of complicated and differentiated artefacts in wood and bone as well as fine stone blades. Specialised implements in pressure-flaking technique make their appearance. Man learned how to produce scrapers, knives, points of various forms and so forth. These were used as hunting weapons as well as instruments for the working of bones, wood and hides. Thus it is clear the Magdalenian Man made use of a number of different wooden implements and utensils of bark, rind and skin. Although many thousands of years before the Magdalenian sewn clothing and foot-gear were known and beads and pendants of stone, shell and bone were used as ornaments, now there appeared a regular 'fashion' in the shape of diadems, bracelets, pierced small stones and adornments of many sorts.

In Magdalenian art we find abstract designs together with animal and plant ornaments. Meanders and swastikas (e.g. the Mesin site in the Ukraine) afford proof that Man already possessed a feeling for symmetry and that he could also count. Especially attractive are the fine bas-reliefs and the engraved groups of animals.

In Magdalenian times the main branches of the existing races were differentiated—as the still rare finds prove. In Europe there lived for the most part the direct descendants of the Cro-Magnons, in Africa typical Negroids and in Asia men with unmistakable Mongoloid traits.

The Men of the Magdalenian Period

In 1914 two burials were unearthed near Obercassel, not far from Bonn. The graves had been dug down into the clayey ground and covered with basalt slabs. The bones had been abundantly sprinkled with red ochre. In one of the graves was the skeleton of a male and in other one of a female. At their heads lay bone artefacts and with the woman was a polishing tool carved at the handle-end with the small head of a marten. With the man was a flat, engraved small head of a horse. No stone implements were found but in both graves were the bones of sacrificed animals. The burials would date from the developed Magdalenian culture.

The woman was young, at most twenty-five years old when she died, but the man was at least fifty. Examination of the skeletons showed that they belonged to descendants of Cro-Magnon Man although they differed from him by a smaller stature. The woman was about 155 centimetres in height and the man some 160 centimetres. The male skull presented the general features of the Cro-Magnon type but differed from the earlier forms by a shorter and higher vault, a more strongly developed supraorbital ridge, a higher face and an extraordinarily massive and wide lower jaw.

The female skull resembled that of the woman from the Cro-Magnon grotto and had the same form of forehead, the low eye-sockets, the short, and only slightly projecting nose, some degree of prognathism and small chin formation. The face was, however, higher, narrower, and more orthognathous, the vault of the skull shorter and higher.

In reconstructing the male skull we purposely 'rejuvenated' it so as to show better the anthropological type. Of the woman's skull only a drawing of the reconstituted head was made.

In 1888 a burial was discovered in south-western France not far from the village of Chancelade (Dordogne), and in the Raymonden grotto. The bones lay at a depth of 1·5 metres and over the grave lay levels of undisturbed cultural horizons belonging to developed early and late phases of the Magdalenian. The individuals lay in a contracted position on the rock-floor of the grotto and the bones were only slightly strewn with earth. The cultural horizons had been formed later on during a prolonged sojourn of Man in the grotto. The archaeological dating of the burial is undoubtedly that of the early phase of the Magdalenian.

The Chancelade skeleton is clearly that of a rather short later form of the Cro-Magnon race. At first it was considered to be a Mongoloid variant of *Homo sapiens*. But this attribution was an error. In the museum the nasal bones had been broken off and lost, so that an appearance of a flattened, Mongoloid face was produced. The skull displays the flattening of the cheek-bones, however, that is characteristic of all Cro-Magnons, but it differs from them by a higher vault, a very high face and the high eye-sockets. And on account of all these features it was thought that the Chancelade skull resembled that of an Eskimo.

The portions preserved of the nasal base and the nose-forehead process of the cheek-bones indicate a very prominent, fine nose, so that we must regard the Chancelade skull as a Europoid type.

The reconstructed head of this man produced a peculiar impression. The face was relatively narrow, high, flattened and had a markedly projecting almost straight nose. It was not the face of a typical Europoid but had lost the old Cro-Magnon features to a considerable extent.

In 1953 the Soviet archaeologist P. I. Boriskovski discovered near the Kostienki site II on the Don a late Magdalenian burial in very poor condition. During the excavation a portion of a collapsed Palaeolithic dwelling was uncovered there, but near it and touching it was a narrower building of oval form constructed of mammoth bones (2·20 metres by 0·55 metres) which had served as the burial vault for human skeletal remains. Some bones—a pelvis, a thigh-bone, shin-bones and bones of the foot—had kept almost their original positions. And from this it was clear that the bodies had been contracted. The legs were drawn up and pressed closely against the chest. The soles of the feet were turned up under the pelvis. In this position the corpse was not laid out but set up.

With the destruction of the upper part of the chamber the skull and the various bones of the upper part of the torso had fallen apart. The whole skeleton was in very bad condition. Only fragments of the skull survived but the facial skeleton was so far intact that not only was its restoration possible but even a reconstruction of the head could be made.

The man of Kostienki II showed the typical Cro-Magnon disharmony between the elongated cranium and the very broad,

The men of Combe-Capelle (*right*) and Cro-Magnon (*left*) belong to the Upper Palaeolithic period. They lived from about 40,000 years ago until about 8000 B.C. They are the first undoubted representatives of *Homo sapiens*.

The reconstruction of the portraits of the Timurids was a difficult task since there was the additional aim of furnishing proof of blood relationship. But an unexpected fact came to the help of Gerasimov. During the reconstruction of Timur's portrait (*below*) he noticed a left-sided plagiocephaly, that is an obliquity in the cranial bones due to abnormal formation of the coronal suture. Above is the completed reconstruction of Timur's portrait. Below Timur's head partially reconstituted.

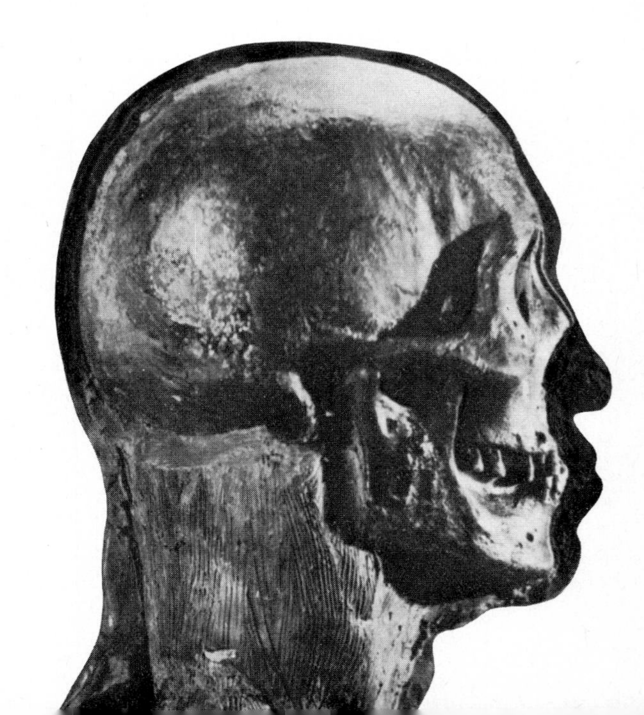

Ulugh-Beg, a grandson of Timur, and the eldest son of Shah-Rukh, was the most outstanding astronomer of central Asia in the 15th century, and the founder of an observatory. He drew up a map of the stars and of the planetary movements. He was murdered at his son's behest. His assassin struck off his head with an oriental sabre. The marks of the blade are to be clearly seen on the neck bones. He must have been buried in the clothes he was wearing when he met his end. His corpse was neither washed nor embalmed.

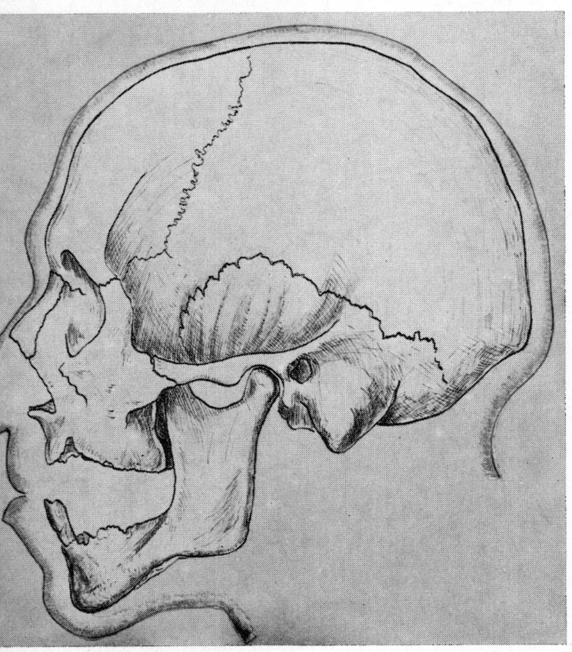

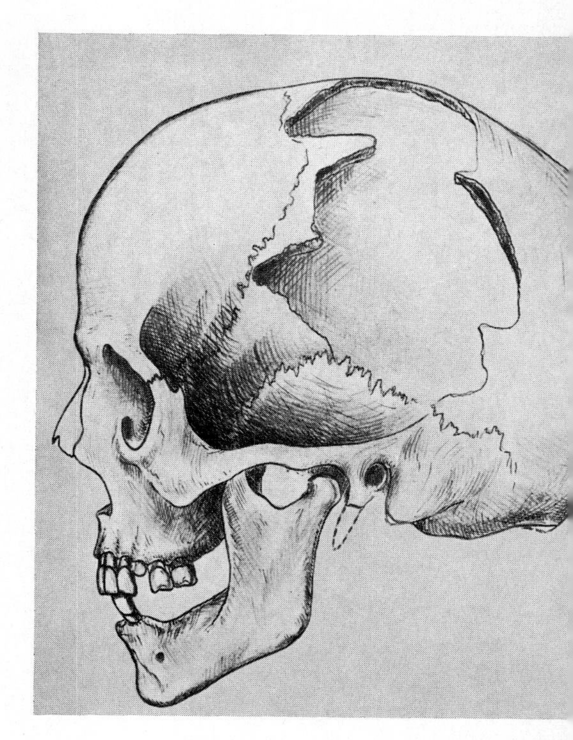

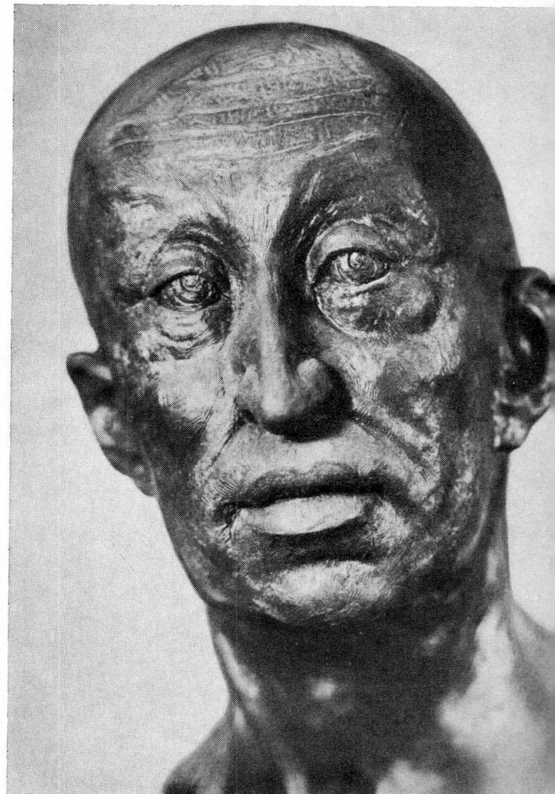

Miranshah, another of Timur's sons, inherited courage and cruelty from his father and he fell in battle. His enemy struck the head from the body and exhibited it. On the base of the skull the traces of a knife could still clearly be seen, and the vault of the skull was damaged when the head was impaled.

short face, but with this the resemblance between the two types ceased. The Kostienki Man was much more like present-day Europoids even if we cannot say that he presented close analogies with any one race of recent Man. The face was orthognathous, short and wide. The broad nose had considerably thick soft parts. The mouth was small and thin-lipped, the chin small but nevertheless projecting. The skeleton belonged to an individual about fifty years old and he measured 165 centimetres in height.

But the reconstructed face showed on the whole no resemblance to the real Cro-Magnon men and the specimen must rather be considered as a new variant of eastern Europoid Cro-Magnon Man of Magdalenian times.

In the year 1930 the well-known Chinese geologist Pei Wen-chung while digging in the upper grotto at Choukoutien came upon several burials. The cultural level contained typical late Magdalenian artefacts of the Siberian-Mongolian province. Not only the stone implements but the bone objects and the ornaments in this grotto were absolutely identical with the objects of the Siberian industry of that period and especially with that of the lower levels at Aftonova Gora near Krasnoiarsk on the Yenissei river.

We had at our disposal a cast of a male skull from the Upper Grotto site. It was big, very massive, dolichocephalic with a high vault, sloping forehead and strongly developed supraorbital region. The face was long and broad but not so flattened as that of the recent Mongoloids of Asia. The nose projected more, the eye-sockets were very low, the cheek-bones broad and resembled the Cro-Magnon form.

In his description of this skull Weidenreich pointed out its resemblance to the Cro-Magnon skulls of western Europe but he also noted some Mongoloid features.

The head reconstructed from this Choukoutien skull had the features of an undifferentiated Mongoloid but it showed no analogy to the present-day Mongoloid faces.

In this connection it may be pointed out that the smallest number of Palaeolithic hominid finds occurs among Mongoloid forms. The most ancient Mongoloid was found by me in 1929 at the Mal'ta site not far from Irkutsk. This interment must have taken place right at the beginning of human settlement in the area, that is to say at a time when the cultural phase was a developed Aurignacian. The skeleton of a child, from three to four years old, was recovered from a dolmen-like construction of limestone. There was a rich collection of grave-gear. Around the child's head was a diadem of mammoth ivory, on the breast a necklace of small pierced stones with ornamental pendants in the form of figures and one in the shape of a flying duck, and in the region of the belly a flat, round stud engraved with parallel wavy lines. On the right arm was a thin curved bracelet. At the feet of the skeleton was a large point made from a mammoth's tusk, stone artefacts, convex burin of Aurignacian type, a point and a scraper. The interment was thickly strewn with red pigment.

Unfortunately the bones were in a wretched state of preservation. Of the skull only fragments of the dolichocephalic cranium, part of the cheek-bones, the teeth and the lower jaw remained. The child was very small; however, some Mongoloid features could be observed.

At the Palaeolithic Aftonova Gora site near Krasnoiarsk a forehead fragment was discovered. If we can judge from the shape of this bone the ancient, original population of the Aftonova Gora region was of an unmistakably Mongoloid character.

This reliable evidence was strengthened by finds from the Mal'ta settlement. We have mentioned that among the works of art of the Aurignacian and Solutrean cultures of Ice Age Europe many female statuettes have been discovered. A first glance at these is enough to convince us that the artists were concerned, above all, to stress typical femininity without wanting to express the individuality of any particular model. Still, despite all the stylisation, one can see clearly enough from all these sculptures that they represent European women.

The female statuettes from Mal'ta on the other hand present a quite different appearance. The artist was concerned above all to depict Mongoloid characteristics, and this is clearly indicated by the proportions of the members and by the broad, flattened Mongoloid faces.

We have now come to the end of our considerations which have allowed us to glance backwards into the past millennia. Many faces of prehistoric Man have passed before us. Some are primitive and animal-like, cunning and malicious, ugly and good-looking, alien and yet also quite familiar.

What has been said above proves that in the Upper Palaeolithic the main lines of the existing races had begun to be fixed.

7 *Portraits of Historical Personages*

The reconstruction of the faces and figures of historical personages is not only interesting for historians, authors, biologists and anthropologists but also for every cultivated human being whatever may be his or her walk of life.

The reconstructions are especially interesting when they form family portraits, that is to say those of men who are linked through blood-relationship. In this connection some quite unexpected problems may crop up both of an historical as well of a personal nature.

For instance, during the making of the Timurids' portraits a discussion arose as to whether Shah-Rukh was a real son of Timur. Timur was, from an anthropological point of view, a typical Mongoloid while Shah-Rukh was pronouncedly Europoid. Historians of central Asia often refer to the dislike the father felt for the son. Hence a legend arose that Shah-Rukh could not have been Timur's actual son.

There could be no doubt as to the authenticity of the skeletons. The bodies lay under gravestones with identificatory inscriptions. Moreover, after the burial of Timur and Shah-Rukh in the Samarkand Gur-i-Emir mausoleum their bodies were not exhumed as the condition of the tombs proved decisively enough.

Here was a difficult problem to solve, proof of paternity. Was this possible after the lapse of five hundred years? Often such a question can only be conditionally answered in the case of living people. All the same we had luck on our side. All the five Timurid skulls at the Gur-i-Emir burial-place display the same anatomical peculiarities despite differences in age and in anthropological types. In the structure of the vaults of the skulls there is repeated the same anomaly, the same asymmetry, a phenomenon due to what is called left-sided plagiocephaly, that is an irregular deformity of half of the coronal suture. Such a striking similarity in the form of all the skulls can be attributed only to heredity.

So Timur was a typical Mongoloid. His grandsons Ulugh-Beg and Mohammed Sultan were 'hybrids' and in type closely resembled the present-day town-dwelling Uzbeks. The sons Shah-Rukh and Miran-Shah possessed unmistakable features of the Tadjik type (Europoid of central Asia). Despite these differences all five of these men belonged through blood-relationship to one family. This fact is undoubted.

Ulugh-Beg and Mohammed Sultan were cousins and each resembled his grandfather. Both the sons of Timur, Shah-Rukh and Miran-Shah looked much alike and furthermore Miran-Shah also resembled his father.

We have no information about Timur's wives. The facial likeness between Shah-Rukh and Miran-Shah and their belonging to one and the same anthropological type seem to confirm the supposition that they were proper brothers.

Often the face reconstituted from the skull does not correspond to well-known portraits of an individual executed during his lifetime. So naturally enough a question is raised about the authenticity of the reconstitution.

Obviously paintings of living models do correspond to their real appearance, but artists create according to prevailing fashion and taste. Indeed, their works of art should not be 'photographic'. There is also another point that is important. Does the researcher in his work not come under the influence of quite definite preconceptions about his subject? Does he not allow himself to be affected by literary evidence or other representations? Does he not reconstruct from a skull, unconsciously perhaps, a portrait corresponding to an imaginary picture that only he regards as authentic?

Of course what must be done in a reconstruction is not to present the lifeless pattern of an abstract anthropological type, but the face of an individual human being with his quite specific features and with proportions that are peculiar to him, so that the portrait can be recognised as his and that of no one else. A visage is like a landscape, unique and unchangeable.

Maria Dostoievskaya

Maria Dostoievskaya, *née* Nechaeiva (1799–1836), was the mother of the author Dostoievski.

In the year 1937 I still did not dare to hope that I should be able to reconstitute from the skull a true portrait of a famous person. At the time I was mostly occupied with making test-reconstructions from the skulls of contemporaries, so as at least to convince myself how complicated the task was that I had to perform.

The reader will remember how I managed to make a test-reconstruction of a Papuan's head at the Moscow University Anthropological Department in the presence of professors and colleagues. Just at this time M. V. Volozkoi told me that he possessed a highly interesting skull, as well as a portrait painted from life, of the person to whom it had belonged.

A few years before a coffin had been opened in a Moscow cemetery. It was pretty certain whose the skeleton was. But Volozkoi who had worked on the skeletal material wanted to assure himself of the identity of the remains, so he handed over to me a skull and explained simply that it had belonged to a woman who had lived a hundred years before and must have been related to a Russian writer.

The skull was in fragments and the occipital bone, together with the base of the skull, was missing. The facial bones were not only badly preserved but their whole surface was split into small pieces, parts of which crumbled at the touch. The teeth were badly affected. Here and there on the skull-vault were some remains of hair parted in the middle. It varied in length from 3 to 7 centimetres (1¼ to 3 inches), was mostly of a greyish-green colour though in places of a faded chestnut-brown. It was brittle and crumbled at the touch.

However, in spite of its condition the skull was so characteristic that a casual glance was enough to afford a summary description of the face.

I was to take the skull with me to Leningrad and there work on it. It had belonged to a young woman who must have died when she was aged about thirty-six or thirty-seven. The face was very broad, the high forehead had strongly developed frontal prominences and was shapely in form. The delicately designed supraorbital area harmonised well enough with the wide, open, almost square eye-orbits. The nasal bones were narrow and deeply implanted beneath the lower margin of the forehead. The nasal aperture was heart-shaped and almost symmetrical. The tip of the nasal bones was well shaped and directed downwards. The finely contoured cheek-bones were only slightly projecting so that they harmonised well with the broad vault of the skull. The upper jaw was well modelled and the teeth closed in a regular scissors-bite. The lower jaw was typically delicate and female although relatively broad. The chin was pointed, fine and sharply defined. Speaking generally, the skull indicated that the young woman had had a broad, high forehead, a wide face, large, shapely eyes, a relatively large nose with an undulating profile and slightly downwards-directed tip. She must also have possessed a mouth of beautiful shape.

So there I was back in Leningrad and beginning my work on the portrait of a woman unknown to me. I reconstructed the main masticatory muscles and then the ridges on the sagittal and horizontal planes of the face, to indicate the thickness of the soft parts. Then I reconstructed first the right- and then the left-hand side of the visage.

Basing myself on the remains of the hair and taking into account the fashion of the 'thirties of the last century, I gave the reconstructed head a sleek covering of hair parted down the middle and caught up at the back into a large 'bun' while I let curled ringlets hang on either side of the face.

When the reconstruction was finished Volozkoi revealed that I had been working on the skull of Feodor Dostoievski's mother. The only known portrait of Maria Dostoievskaya is one executed in pastel by the artist Popov. It is in the typical tradition of portrait-painting at the early part of the nineteenth century and shows her at about the age of nineteen to twenty-two with the coiffure and dress of approximately the year 1820. Maria Dostoievskaya was still a young woman when she died in 1836, that is to say about thirteen or fourteen years later.

Despite a difference in age and a certain stylisation in the portrait, it and my reconstruction represented quite undoubtedly one and the same person and both pictures also showed a likeness to the paintings of Maria Dostoievskaya's children. So, once again, I was able to prove my method to be right.

Years later I handed over the reconstruction to the Feodor Dostoievski Museum and on this occasion was able to see for the first time the death-mask of the author. The resemblance between the two was unmistakable.

Yaroslav the Wise

Prince Yaroslav Vladimirovich (978–1054), the son of Prince Vladimir Sviatoslavovich and his wife Rogneda, was from 1019 to 1054 Prince of Kiev. It was during his reign that the old Russian State became stronger and more flourishing. Under Prince Yaroslav the oldest part of the legal code was also produced, known as *Ruskaya Pravda* (Russian Law).

In January 1939 a marble tomb ascribed to Yaroslav the Wise in the Sophia Cathedral at Kiev was opened in the presence of a special commission consisting of a number of archaeologists and historians including V. V. Ginsburg the anthropologist.

In the tomb were found the skeletons of two adults and a number of bones belonging to a child aged from two to three. The bones lay in considerable disorder but it was possible to see that the skulls of both adult skeletons faced westwards. No portions of textiles were discovered nor were there any other objects.

On closer examination one of the skeletons proved to be that of a man and the other of a woman. The former was that of an individual aged about seventy and some of the bones were pathologically deformed. The remains, however, were tolerably well preserved. The man was of middling height (172 centimetres or 68 inches) and of medium build. He must have limped on his right leg and the sound left leg was stouter, no doubt through compensatory formation. A number of features indicated that the lameness must have occurred during the man's younger days—the displacement and the elongation of the neck of the right femur, the general asymmetry of the pelvis, deformation of the backbone, etc. Clearly in his later years the man must have been very lame. The whole weight of his body bore down on the left leg so that he would have needed the help of a stick when he walked and must have avoided violent movements, especially of the torso. So it was sufficiently well proved that the skeleton in the sarcophagus of the Sophia Cathedral really was that of Yaroslav the Wise. The chronicles mention his lameness.

After an examination of the skull Ginsburg concluded that it approximated closest to the Slav type, especially to that of the Novgorod Slavs of the eleventh to twelfth centuries. It differed however from this type by the height of the face and the slight deepening of the jaw fossae which are characteristic features of short-headed (brachycephalic) skulls. V. V. Ginsburg is inclined to regard these features as due to hybridisation between long-headed and short-headed types.

G. F. Debez, the anthropologist, has pointed out that this mixed type appeared during the first centuries of our era in the south-east of the present U.S.S.R. It is, however, not improbable that the idiosyncracies of the skull may be due to the presence of certain Nordic elements. Nevertheless the skeleton despite the features in question was obviously of local origin and did not belong to an immigrant from the north.

Maybe these facts are of use in helping to clear up one of the most interesting questions in Russian history—what was the origin of the first princes of the Kievan state?

The remains of Yaroslav the Wise were also examined by the radiologist Professor D. G. Rochlin but I learned of the results of his investigations only after I had completed my work, for in this same year the skull of Yaroslav the Wise was handed over to me so that a reconstruction of his portrait might be made.

Several teeth were missing, the left cheek-bone with the adjacent portion of the upper jaw were broken off. An examination of the edges of the sockets and of a few teeth convinced me that the missing teeth must have fallen out after death.

The replacement of missing skull fragments is an extremely difficult task and one involving great responsibility. In the present case however my work was facilitated since the missing portions could be reconstituted from the other side of the skull that was intact. So the upper jaw and the cheek-bone on the left side were modelled from the corresponding bones on the other side. In doing this I had to pay particular attention to the copying of the microrelief of the missing parts. Since the alveolar region of both jaws was, however, excellently preserved, the replacement of the missing teeth presented no difficulty.

The portions of the skull which had to be replaced were modelled in very hard wax so that they should remain unaltered during the work of reconstituting the soft parts of the face. The form of the skull-cap was between the elliptic and the ovoid and the

K

bregma was rectangular and somewhat square. The flatness of the low vault was accentuated by a sloping forehead. The back of the head was rounded and its relief very marked. The mastoid processes were strongly developed and indicated powerful neck muscles. The almost completely obliterated cranial sutures pointed to the individual's advanced age.

The form of the face was ovoid, the cheek-bones were well defined, relatively narrow and moderately projecting; the forehead was moderately high and fairly broad with only a slightly developed relief. The superciliary ridges (*Arcus superciliares*) were only slightly marked and short. The root of the nose had an index of three. The eye-orbits were large, of medium height, angular, with strongly sloping margins. The nose projected sharply and in profile was slightly curved, the bridge of the nose was high, the root narrow.

The alveolar arch of the upper jaw was narrow and slightly prognathous. The lower jaw, with massive, steeply rising ramus, had a sharply projecting chin. The jutting chin was accentuated by a considerable degree of alveolar prognathism. When the jaws were closed the teeth of the lower jaw projected to a marked degree.

The teeth in general showed only a moderate degree of wear and especially if we take into account the age of the individual (over seventy) may indeed be accounted only slight. At his death Yaroslav had all his teeth. No traces of decay were to be seen.

For the reconstruction of the head of Yaroslav the Wise I proceeded thus: after I had fixed the lower jaw (taking into account the form of the dentition) to the upper jaw, I supplied the principal masticatory muscles. According to the evidence I got by examination of the neck vertebrae and the base of the skull, I gave the head the characteristic position and then affixed it to a wooden framework especially prepared for the purpose.

Yaroslav's right-sided lameness determined a certain oblique position of the torso and a peculiar poise of the head which was held forward owing to the compensatory flexion of the backbone and the slope of the shoulders.

After the modelling of the throat and the consolidation of the skull I began the reconstitution of the head.

After the face had been completed the ear had to be dealt with.

The size and shape of the mastoid process, the direction of the ascending ramus of the lower jaw as well as the length measurement of the nose, were clues to its form.

So the mask was produced. It is worth noting that the portrait up to this stage of the reconstruction was undoubtedly like the original face since all the details of the reproduction were based on reliable factors.

Further work was based on a subjective appreciation of the subject to be reconstructed and cannot claim to be absolutely true to nature.

The way Yaroslav wore his hair could be determined only by a portrait or from a mention in chronicles. After long discussions among historians it was decided to show the Prince with hair cut in a circle round the head and with a pointed beard. The shape of the eyebrows could be determined with certainty from the form of the supraorbital region.

The clothing and head-covering were indicated by an examination of twelfth-century frescoes and were copied from these and other archaeological material.[1]

Each of the scientists gave, at the end of his report, a more or less exhaustive description of the Prince's appearance. Neither Ginsburg nor Rochlin or any of those present at the meeting had seen my work, nevertheless the descriptions given corresponded astonishingly well with my reconstructed portrait of Yaroslav which was shown only after my paper had been read.

Andrei Bogolyubski

Andrei Bogolyubski, son of Prince Yuri Dologoruki and his second wife, daughter of the Polovtsian Prince Aepa, was born about 1110 and was murdered in 1175 when he was Prince of Vladimir.

[1] At the Institute of Material Culture the following scientists read papers:

1 V. Ginsburg (on the anthropological examination of the skeleton of Yaroslav the Wise).

2 D. Rochlin, 'The results of the anatomical and radiographical examination of the skeleton of Yaroslav the Wise'.

3 M. Gerasimov, 'An attempted reconstruction of the physical appearance of Yaroslav the Wise'.

Andrei Bogolyubski was an outstanding feudal ruler and one of the great personalities of the twelfth century. He was the first Russian prince who endeavoured to abolish the autonomous principalities and to create a united Russian State with a new capital at the city of Vladimir on the Klysma.

His reign was a time of political disorders. Kiev gradually lost its importance—not without Prince Andrei's interference. As soon as he established himself at the town of Suzdal on the Klysma, he began at once to steadily suppress the independance of the Suzdel boyars and in doing this he was supported by the traders, the merchants and the artisans of the towns. In 1169 Kiev, the mother-city of Russia, was overthrown.

Prince Andrei subdued Murom and Ryazan and strove to acquire a still greater extension of his power. But he was not able to carry out his plans. On one summer's night in 1175 the Prince of Vladimir fell a victim to a conspiracy of the boyars and was treacherously assassinated in the Bogolyubski Palace.

In the chronicles we can read not only about the Prince of Vladimir's political activities but also quite lengthy descriptions of his character although these vary from source to source and are often coloured by subjective prejudice.

According to the statements of the historians Roshkov and Soloviov Prince Andrei was rash and often rushed into the turmoil of the fray . . . 'Andrei would forget himself in the excitement of conflict and would risk his life for the fury of battle intoxicated him.'

The proof of these statements can be read from his skeleton for it shows traces of old wounds on both arms—evidence of his valour.

'He was the prince of all things and deeds. Only a lack of moderation clouded his mind. He was filled with self-conceit and when he was enraged he spoke very harsh words. He hated those nearest him and they flattered him but spoke deceitfully about him. Thus they antagonised him against brothers and alienated him from those who stood nearest to his father. So he banished some and imprisoned others and thus arose bitter conflict in the lands of Rostov and Suzdal.'

The chronicles contain lengthy descriptions of the circumstances of Prince Andrei's death and these accounts provide valuable indications for identifying his skeleton. The records tell us that Andrei was imperious, implacable and irritable. His arrogance was shown by the haughty way he carried his head.

Both the policy and the autocratic behaviour of Andrei excited increasing discontent among the boyars. But something to force them to open rebellion was lacking. An occasion was soon found. A near relation of Andrei's wife, one Kuchkovich, was executed. The word went round . . . 'Today he's had Kuchkovich killed and tomorrow it will be our turn. Don't let us forget that' . . . so a conspiracy was formed in which (according to the Ipatiev list) Kuchkov took part ('the chief murderer'), Anbal Yasin, Yakim Kuchkovich, Yefrem Monsovich and fifteen others.

In the middle of the night of 29th June 1175 the conspirators forced their way into the princely residence, overcame the palace guards and moved up to the Prince's bedroom on the first storey. The door was locked. They knocked. Andrei awoke and asked who was there. The answer was 'Prokopi' but Andrei knew his servant's voice well enough and realised at once that it could not be Prokopi. His suspicions were aroused. He reached for his weapon but his sword had disappeared. 'Anbal the door-keeper had removed it.' (So in the words of the chronicler.) The door was then burst open and two of the conspirators flung themselves on the unarmed Bogolyubski who defended himself stubbornly. 'But was the prince strong . . .' He threw down one of his assailants —'The prince overcame one of them . . .'—but then the others rushed into the room and stabbed their fellow-conspirator as he lay on the floor. When they realised their mistake they turned on Andrei and 'slashed him with sword and sabre.' The prince stumbled to the ground and the conspirators, thinking he was dead, retired with the body of their accomplice. But Andrei was still living. He tried to reach the spiral staircase leading downstairs. And then groaned aloud—'he began to groan from pain and agony and to speak'—the conspirators heard him and turned back; they found the prince and 'dealt him the death-blow. Piotr Kutschkov then hacked off Andrei's right hand and drove a lance through his ribs'.

Since Prince Andrei Bogolyubski had built several splendid places of worship in the Suzdal land, the Church valued him very highly and his martyr's death served as a pretext for proclaiming him a saint.

Andrei's mortal remains were interred in the Uspenski monastery at Vladimir and were later removed to the archaeological museum in the same town.

D. G. Rochlin and V. S. Maikova-Stroganova by means of radiographical examination of the skeleton determined the circumstances of the murder. Their researches not only proved the authenticity of the remains but also supported the trustworthiness of the chroniclers' account of the prince's death. In a masterly fashion the figure of this man was delineated who had been dead for over 700 years.

The scientists discovered on the skeleton, besides the marks of old wounds, the traces of many others caused by sharp instruments, that is inflicted by the sword and sabre when he was assassinated. On the skull in the region of the right temporal bone was a lozenge-shaped hole, at the back of the head were the marks of a blow made by a sharp blade, there were traces of wounds on the wrist-bones, on the bones of the left upper arm, the left shoulder-blade and the left hip-bone.

After examination of the 'fresh' wounds on the skeleton of Andrei Bogolyubski the researchers came to the conclusion that only one of his enemies could have dealt him a blow from the front. It was relatively slight and the sword or sabre reached the left collar-bone. All the other wounds were inflicted from the side or from behind or when Andrei was lying on the ground. In a duel or on the battlefield this would have been impossible so obviously he was the victim of a murderous assault by several persons wielding various weapons.

Andrei Bogolyubski was above middle height (about 170 centimetres or 5 feet 8 inches), well built and young-looking for his age. In 1941 V. V. Ginsburg undertook an anthropological examination of the skull which increased our information about the prince's appearance. The biological age of the remains did not correspond to the calendrical. The relief of the skull was clearly marked. The obliteration of the sutures had just begun in the region of the lateral part of the coronal. The teeth were well preserved and their crowns showed signs of only moderate wear.

No decay was observable. Judging from the skull the age of the individual would be set at from forty-five to fifty years. But the chroniclers' tell us that Andrei Bogolyubski was about sixty-three years old when he was murdered. This disparity between the apparent and the real age may be explained, the radiologists think, by some disturbance of the endocrine glandular system.

From the racial point of view the skull generally speaking can be characterised as north Europoid. It shows resemblances to the Slav skulls discovered in the tumulus (kurgan) graves, but Andrei's cranium also possesses some features which show Mongoloid influence. This is not surprising in view of what the chronicles tell us about the relationship of Bogolyubski's mother to the Polovtsian Prince Aepa.

The skull is rather elongated and the vault roof-shaped and low, the forehead is retreating with only a slightly marked supra-orbital region. The face is of medium length, the orbits rounded in shape, rather long horizontally, relatively narrow and with sharp margins above and on either side. The cheek-bones project only slightly. The nose is rather elongated, and projected sharply forwards from under the retreating forehead . . . the interorbital width is considerable.

As seen from the side the orbits are remarkable for the marked projection of the lower margins. Taken in conjunction with the slightly projecting cheek-bones and the wide roof of the nasal bones such a combination of features does lend the whole visage a Mongoloid character.

The flattening of the base of the skull in its region of articulation and the deformity of the second and third neck vertebrae caused a somewhat lofty poise of the head which lent Andrei a proud, unapproachable appearance which the chronicles repeatedly mention.

In order to be able to reproduce the face more exactly from the skull I devised a special system for preliminary graphical reconstruction. The asymmetry of the face and skull as well as the soft parts of the face were determined by a series of investigations accompanied by horizontal sections of the head.

With a craniometer I prepared several horizontal contours of the skull (parallel to the eye-ear plane) and drew on these the soft parts. In this way the profile designs of the horizontal section of the face could be reconstructed.

The rest once again was based on hypothetical statements and consisted in the artistic completion of the documentary mask. The question as to whether Andrei Bogolyubski should be shown with or without a beard and how he should be clothed were subjects of long discussions at the Institute for the History of Material Culture of the U.S.S.R. Academy of Sciences. Finally I gave Andrei a wavy head of hair and showed his beard worn in the Mongol fashion which suited his general type admirably. The clothing I fashioned with the help of material from the Vladimir Museum, and from portions of stuff which N. N. Voronin, an outstanding authority on early Russian history, considers may have belonged to Andrei Bogolyubski.

8 *The Timurids*

On the occasion of the 500th jubilee of the great Uzbek poet Alisher Navoi the tombs of certain historical personages were opened in the Gur-i-Emir mausoleum at Samarkand.

In the year 1941 an expedition under the direction of T. N. Kary-Niyasov, member of the Uzbekistan Socialist Soviet Republic Academy of Sciences, visited the burial-place. The expedition was entrusted with the following task: to open the graves of the Timurids, to ascertain the circumstances of the interments (so as to confirm or to check information available from documentary sources); to throw light on burial ritual, to undertake anthropological investigations into the mortal remains and, finally, to establish documentary portraits of the Timurids from their skulls. Among other things proof of the blood relationship between Timur and Shah-Rukh was to be sought.

From literary historical documents it was known that the Timurid burials in the main vault were not primary, that is to say the remains were brought to Samarkand at various times and from various places for interment.

The construction of the Gur-i-Emir mausoleum was begun, at Timur's command, in 1404, but the mausoleum was completed only after Timur's death. The monument was intended for the tomb of his beloved grandson Mohammed Sultan, whom Timur desired to be his successor. But Mohammed Sultan met with an untimely death in Persia aged only twenty-nine. His mortal remains were taken to Onik, a town not far from Erzerum, and there buried. Later the body was placed in a new coffin and removed to Sultania in Persia where it was re-buried. Two years afterwards, in 1404, the remains were brought to Samarkand, and interred in a medresseh (Moslem high school) which Mohammed Sultan had had erected during his lifetime.

Timur himself died in February 1405 in the town of Otrar (today a settlement near the Timur railway station on the Orenburg line). He was on his way to an invasion of China. His body was carried to Samarkand and buried in the medresseh where his grandson also lay.

On the completion of the Gur-i-Emir the bodies of Timur and of Mohammed Sultan were transferred to the burial vault. An anonymous writer recorded that Timur's body was embalmed . . .

'The corpse was be-sprinkled with perfumes, rose-water, musk and camphor.' Ibn-Arabshah wrote that the 'body after some time was placed in a steel sarcophagus which had been made by a master artist from Shiraz. The sarcophagus is said to have been encrusted with gold and silver.'

In 1407 Timur's third son Miran-Shah fell in battle near Tabriz in Azerbaijan. At first the body was buried at Surhab. Later on it was transferred to Timur's birthplace, the little town of Kesh. It was not until the 'sixties or 'seventies of the fifteenth century that Miran-Shah's remains reached the Gur-i-Emir mausoleum at Samarkand.

Timur's youngest son Shah-Rukh died in 1447. His remains were also later brought to Samarkand and interred at the right-hand side of Timur's grave.

On 28th October 1449 Timur's grandson Ulugh-Beg was assassinated. His body eventually found its place at the foot of Timur's grave in the mausoleum.

These were the graves of the Timurids that the expedition had now to open. Since all of the bodies with the exception of that of Miran-Shah lay in stone sarcophagi, the programme was as follows: to open the graves, to identify them, and to preserve the remains and any objects which might be in the sarcophagi. Only Miran-Shah's grave, which was just a chamber dug in the ground and filled with earth, demanded the usual clearance layer by layer.

The removal of the gravestones, the recovery of textiles and bone fragments as well as their preservation was undertaken by me. Fabrics and wood were preserved by V. N. Kononov. V. A. Shishkin dealt with the archaeological side of the investigation and he also was responsible for the complete report on the results of the work done. A. A. Semenov studied and deciphered with extraordinary exactitude the inscriptions on the stone slabs over the graves as well as the writing on the memorial stones over the tombs in the upper chamber of the mausoleum. L. V. Oshanin assumed the task of examining the bones from the anatomical and anthropological point of view.

The expedition produced a detailed photographic record of the whole operation and this was done by the photographer I. P.

Savalin. The filming was undertaken by Koyumov under the direction of N. A. Kims.

We remained at the Gur-i-Emir from 16th to 24th June 1941. The clerical work was continued at Tashkent until October 1943.

The bones of the Timurids were then replaced in their original positions in their sarcophagi and in each grave was put an exhumation record drawn up in four languages (Uzbek, Russian, Persian and English). The documents written in India ink on Uzbek parchment (nineteenth-century Kokand paper) were hermetically sealed up in very thick glass tubes, thoroughly disinfected and filled with nitrogen. The tubes were then deposited in small marble model sarcophagi with tight-fitting covers consolidated with a special central Asian mortar.

The portions of woven stuff, Timur's wooden coffin, the remains of his hair as well as all the written reports and the Timurids busts are now preserved in the Navoi Literature Museum of the Uzbek Republic Academy of Sciences in Tashkent.

Timur

Timur (Tamerlane), the greatest conqueror of central Asia (1336–1405), when thirty-six years old assumed the style of Emir of Ulus Jagatai. From 1369 to 1380 he undertook nine campaigns in Turkestan, subjected part of Afghanistan while from 1380 to 1393 he waged war on Persia. In 1391–5 he defeated Toktamish the Khan of the Golden Horde. In 1393 he conquered Bagdad and Mesopotamia, in 1398–9 part of India and in 1401 he subjected part of Syria. As we have said he died on his way to an invasion of China.

Timur's grave lay in the middle of the mausoleum's crypt. The gravestone was a roughly hewn slab of grey limestone on which was placed a thin layer of onyx bearing an exceedingly fine incised inscription which was deciphered by Professor A. A. Semenov. The completed text was published in 1948. Here is an extract from it:

'This is the grave of the most mighty Sultan and most noble Khan preserved in safety and protection, the Emir Timur, son of the Emir Teragai, son of the Emir Barkul, son of the Emir Aklangis, son of the Emir Idshil, son of the Emir Idamchi Berlas, son of the Emir Kachulai Khan, son of the Emir Tumanai' (then after a good deal more) 'Ghengis Khan, son of the Emir Kabul Kahn, son of the Emir Yesukai Bahadur, son of the Emir Bartag Bahadur, son of the Emir Kabul Khan, son of Emir Tumanai, son of the Emir Bug, his mother Alan Kuva. And there was as is related no adultery on her part, but it was the fruit of pure light [radiated] from [one of the] descendants of the Lion [Asad], Allah the Conqueror, Alia the son of Abu Taliba—thus may Allah confer honour upon his visage.'

Thus Timur and Genghis Khan (Jenghiz Khan) would have been descended from a common ancestor, the Mongol Emir Tumanai, from whom one line through his son Kachulai led to Timur while another line from his son Kaidu led to Genghis Khan.

Under the slab could be seen a layer about 10 centimetres (4 inches) thick of mortar which covered the diagonal massive limestone blocks. The walls of the death-chamber were also composed of great blocks of limestone. The flooring consisted of one large slab. The chamber was 228 centimetres (7 feet 7 inches) long, 90 centimetres (about 3 feet) high and measured in width 83 centimetres (about 2 feet 9 inches) at the head and at the foot 74·5 centimetres (say 2 feet 6 inches).

Inside was a wooden coffin of the same shape as those still used today. Over the coffin were the remains of a dark-blue covering of brocade interwoven with extracts from the Koran in silver thread. The coffin of Mohammed Sultan was also covered with the same stuff, thus affording a proof that the two bodies were interred in the Gur-i-Emir at the same time. Timur's coffin of juniper-wood was held together with strong, thick, four-edged, large-headed nails which, however, were completely rusted. When the coffin was opened there rose towards us an overpowering odour of camphor and of other presumably preservative resinous substances.

Within the coffin lay a skeleton on its back with folded hands and outstretched legs. The skull lay on its left side, the face turned toward Mecca.

The anonymous chronicle was thus confirmed. The corpse of Timur had been embalmed. But Ibn-Arabshah's reference to a 'steel coffin' was not proved, neither was the information of Sharaf-ed-din Yasi who asserted that Timur's face was turned towards Said Barak.

Timur was interred in a position usual with Moslem burials. The bones, here and there, were covered with small pieces of woven stuff. On the head, the neck and the hips were the remains of mummified muscles and skin tissue. The finger-bones and the small bones of the feet were somewhat displaced and all the bones were covered with a thin layer of fine loam. In many places on the pelvic-bones and the skull there were needle-shaped concretions of gypsum formed by evaporation of water.

The skull was carefully removed and dried for three hours out of doors in the shade. After that I could begin the work of preservation. It was bathed in wax and colophonium. During the restoration what hair remained on the head, the eyebrows, the lips and the lower part of the face was removed carefully.

One of the most important tasks before the expedition was to ascertain by documentary proof the identity of the skeleton that lay in Timur's grave.

The peoples of the East have left us hundreds of legends concerning the great fifteenth-century conqueror. The very name of the iron Lame Man struck terror in the hearts of men not only in central Asia but also in lands as far away as China and India. The fame of his fabulous riches reached as far as Europe. His biographers were tireless in extolling his great deeds and his campaigns, but in their descriptions of his appearance they were unfortunately far too brief. Many of the statements about his face and figure are moreover contradictory and obscure.

According to Ibn-Arabshah, Timur, the son of Taragai of the stock of Berlas (a Turkified Mongol race), would have been born in 1334 not far from the town of Kesh (Kish) or Shahr-i-Sabz.

From the evidence of the chroniclers it would appear that in 1362 during a fight against the Turkomans, near Sassian, Timur received an arrow-wound and thenceforth until his death limped on his right foot. His right hand was also injured by arrows. In the same year (according to Clavijo's account) he lost two fingers of his right hand. So he was at less than thirty years of age, already a cripple, but nevertheless this did not prevent him from exercising unprecedented power. His contemporaries described him as a red-bearded man of tall stature and extraordinary bodily strength. He was sixty-nine years of age when he set off on the expedition against China and he died on 18th February 1405.

Not one even approximately true representation of the great conqueror has come down to us. The numerous miniatures of later times (and mostly of Iranian and Indian origin) are so different from one another that they can claim no title to authenticity. Written records are also very scanty. The note that Timur descended from the Berlas must serve as evidence and renders unnecessary a close checking of the Indian and Persian miniatures which all depict Timur with Indo-European features and a black beard.

The skeleton in the Gur-i-Emir grave was that of a powerfully built man who, for a Mongoloid, was of comparatively high stature (about 170 centimetres or, say, 5 feet 8 inches). Even during the excavations the researchers noticed certain pathological peculiarities in the skeleton. Closer examination revealed that the bones of the right arm, at the elbow-joint, had grown together so that the arm was rather bent. All the three bones had formed so to speak an inseparable whole. The deformation was so developed that the damaged bone covered the surface of the joints and formed a large excrescence over them. This defect in the elbow was compensated by a marked growth of the upper epiphysis of the shoulder-bones and corresponding changes in the shoulder-blade. So despite his pronounced pathological condition he must not have suffered from loss of movability of his right arm at the shoulder-joint. The state of the bones also allowed it to be seen that the arm not only functioned but was still quite strong. It was the stiffness in his right arm that probably gave rise to the legend that Timur had only one arm.

Despite most careful examination neither pathologists, anatomists nor medical experts could discover a diagnosis for a disease which could have caused so great a change in the elbow-joint. Most of them however were inclined to attribute the phenomenon to a tubercular origin. But according to the reports of all the specialists the ankylosis must have made so much progress that Timur in the last years of his life must no longer have been able to feel any sensation in his right arm.

Without venturing to contradict the findings of the experts, I would, however, note that the evidence of the chroniclers about Timur having been wounded by arrows is undoubtedly confirmed by a mark on the lower epiphysis of the right shoulder-bone on its inner surface. At this spot, in fact, a chip was clearly to be seen which was screened by a later ankylosis.

Timur's lameness was also proved. The right thigh as well as the shank (leg from the knee downwards) were quite pathological. The knee-cap was knitted together with the thigh-bone so that the leg could not be fully stretched out. Later, on the knee-cap and on the epiphysis appeared additional formations but these could not compensate for the defect in the knee.

A comparison of the right leg with the left showed that the bones were in length and in size markedly different from one another and also that the shortness of the right leg could not only be attributed to the position of the knee-joint. The thigh-bones of the sound left leg were characterised by their massiveness and strong relief, whereas the right leg appeared not only shorter but slenderer and weaker.

The experts noted some slight pathological changes in the right heel-bone and a deformation of the second metatarsal bone. The remaining foot-bones were sound.

Timur's vertebrae, ribs and breast-bone showed traces of more or less marked compensatory processes which somewhat mitigated his pronounced lameness. Quite obviously the whole torso was displaced. The left shoulder was considerably higher than the right without the proud poise of the head being affected. The pathological changes must have appeared in later life but this does not correspond to what the written records tell us, namely that Timur's lameness was due to severe wounds received in his youth.

Although the pathological processes which modified the skeleton foundation of his body to such a degree must have been of long standing, it is noteworthy that real marks of senility, accompanied by a weakening of the organism, were hardly to be seen in the skeleton of this man of sixty-nine years of age. The slight osteophyte formation (taking into account Timur's age) only brings out the juvenility of the skeleton as a whole.

Timur was fond of riding and often did not get out of the saddle for a whole day. Maybe this caused the marked curvature of his bad leg? It is, however, quite possible that on horseback he felt his physical infirmities less and also was able to maintain his proud attitude.

The massiveness and strength of the sound bones, their strongly developed relief, the breadth of the shoulders, the size of the chest, and the relatively high stature, all afford grounds for supposing that Timur was an exceedingly robust man. Despite his athletic muscles he must have been lean which is natural enough if we remember that an unsettled life of warfare with its hardships, deprivations and its contingencies is hardly likely to lead to obesity.

A large portion of the left parietal bone of Timur's skull was destroyed by gypsum salts, but still a complete picture of the skull shape could be obtained. The horizontal projection showed a spheroid form. A certain indistinctness in the drawing was to be explained by a considerable natural deformation, owing to the irregular position of the coronal suture. Owing to this there was present a so-called left-sided plagiocephaly which resulted in right-sided development of the skull. Seen in profile the vault was globular but the back of the head did not project, and the occipital protuberance was slightly uneven. The moderately developed *arcus superciliares* (superciliary ridges) hardly projected over the middle of the orbits. The forehead was steep and showed a well marked protuberance. It was noticeable that the superciliary ridges did not run parallel with the margins of the orbits but their outer edges tended upwards towards the protuberances of the forehead. The orbits themselves were large and rounded with markedly projecting, relatively fine, but blunted margins. Although the supraorbital region was relatively little developed, the glabella was very prominent. The face had a regular ovoid shape with only slightly developed cheek-bones.

The nasal root was high, the nasal spine slightly undulating. The wide nasal aperture had the form of a heart. The anterior nasal bone was only slightly developed, a little raised, as was also the sharp under-margin of the nasal opening.

All the main phases of work on the reconstruction of Timur's portrait were photographically recorded and after the model of the left side of the head was completed a cast was prepared which documented that stage of the reconstitution process. A second cast was made after the modelling of the whole head was finished.

Since the remains of Timur were exceptionally well preserved the hair could be reconstructed accurately. As we know that Timur died while on a campaign, it may probably be inferred that, contrary to usual custom, his head was not shaved but his hair was worn rather long. On the temples and behind the ears it measured about 3 centimetres (about 1 inch and a quarter) and on the backbone at the most 1½ centimetres (about three-quarters of an inch). The hair was stiff, thick and of a reddish-brown or reddish grey colour, but mostly dark.

The eyebrows were not so well preserved. All the same from what remained an indication of their general shape could be obtained—and reproduced. The few well-preserved hairs varied in length from 12 to 14 millimetres, they were noticeably curly and of a dark-brown colour.

The moustache was lost. However in the alveolar region of the upper jaw and on the right side was a spot of mildew which showed small fragments of hair and clearly indicated the contour of the moustache. Timur apparently wore his moustache long and not cut above the lip. Such a style was contrary to the then prevailing fashion and to the rules of the *Shariah,* but later on, some old Uzbek experts in Koranic teaching stated that the rules in question certainly did not apply to soldiers.

On the left side of the lower jaw there were still some hairs of the beard; they were not displaced and allowed the contour of the beard on cheeks and chin to be clearly determined. Timur's small, thick beard was cut into the form of a wedge. The hair was stiff, almost straight and thick. The colour was reddish but strongly streaked with grey. Under the magnifying glass the hair-colour was shown as natural and not due to henna-dye. Many of the hairs were in places colourless while others were quite grey.

Costume and head-dress were reconstituted from miniatures and from original robes dating from the time of the Timurid dynasty.

Shah-Rukh

Shah-Rukh, Timur's youngest son, was born on 21st August 1377 and died on 12th March 1447.

Shah-Rukh's grave lies on the right of Timur's and is covered with a slab of splendidly worked grey marble whose polished surface bears an inscription with Shah-Rukh's name and the date of his birth: 15 Rabia kul-Ashirs of the year 779 dating from Mohammed's Hegira, and the date of his death 4 Dhu'l Hija of the year 850 after the Hegira.

From the inscription it would also appear that Shah-Rukh's remains were brought to Samarkand by his daughter Payanda Sultan Bika and that it was she also who erected the gravestone (A. A. Semenov). According to other records (V. V. Barthold) Shah-Rukh died in western Persia and his body was, first of all, taken to Herat and there buried in a medresseh built by his wife Gauchar-Shad. It was not until 1448 when Ulugh-Beg for a short time occupied Herat, that he had his father's body transferred to Samarkand.

In a paper entitled 'Inscriptions from the gravestones of Timur and his successors in the Gur-i-Emir' A. A. Semenov refers to these discrepancies in the presentation of the facts.

V. A. Shishkin is of the opinion that the contradiction is only apparent and can, it would seem, be referred to the shortness of the inscription. Payanda Sultan Bika was indeed Ulugh-Beg's sister in the whole blood and might well have taken care of her father's mortal remains—as would appear from the inscription.

The heavy grave-slab weighing dozens of *pouds* (a Russian *poud* is 16·38 kilogrammes) was raised by means of pulley and tackle and rolled to one side on wooden cylinders.

On the floor of the sarcophagus lay, with the left shoulder

somewhat raised and leaning against the wall, the mortal remains of Shah-Rukh. They were covered with a layer of fine loess which formed a thin, scale-like, cracked crust.

Old inhabitants of Samarkand reported that when building operations were undertaken in the Gur-i-Emir during the years from 1840 to 1870, an irrigation canal near the mausoleum was blocked and the water from this source streamed into the mausoleum and was noticed only when the whole of the crypt was under water. The *aryk* or irrigation channel was repaired as soon as possible and the water emptied out of the grave-vault, but some water had already penetrated into the sarcophagi where it evaporated. That the evaporation had lasted some time was indicated by the presence of fine, needle-shaped formations of gypsum on some parts of the bodies buried in the vault.

When the sarcophagus was opened Shah-Rukh's skeleton was seen to be covered with pieces of textile in bad condition. Between the bones were small portions of mummified muscular fibres which crumbled at the slightest touch. The body seems, then, to have undergone a process of mummification.

As a result of the water penetrating into the grave, the muscle fibres were practically all destroyed and the skeleton was completely bare. Under the left shoulder was a cushion of earth, the skull rested on the right cheek-bone and was turned facing Mecca. The arms were outstretched as were the closely joined legs . . . the hand- and feet-bones were not much displaced so that their original positions could be quite well determined.

In the region of the breast and pelvis were collections of granules. Upon the head lay a bundle of small, leathery leaves looking like those of tea or rhododendron but which on examination proved to be those of sweet basil, a plant with a strong, pleasant smell which today is still very common in central Asia. The leaves were pressed together into a pad as though they had once been contained in a small sachet. Quite near the head was a wooden pen-case like those used by schoolboys. It was filled with hundreds of tiny, well-polished stones which were mostly of a regular elongated form. Their rounded edges and their polish indicated a marine origin.

The skeleton was in a splendid state of preservation. It was thoroughly examined from the anthropological point of view and the results of the examination were published by Professor L. V. Oshanin (University of Tashkent) and his assistant V. Sisinkova.

Some specific peculiarities of the skull are of especial interest since they can throw light on the origins and descent of Shah-Rukh. As we have mentioned more than once he came of Berlas stock and he possessed the features of a Mongoloid although they were attenuated through hybridisation as could be especially noted in the facial bones. A superficial glance at Shah-Rukh's skull was enough to show that the main features were those of another racial type. Shah-Rukh indeed was a typical representative of the brachycephalic Europoid, the so-called Ferghana-Pamir type which is so characteristic of central Asia.

According to outstanding authorities on the documentary sources for Timurid times (Barthold, Masson, Yakubovski and Semenov) the chronicles record the names of none of Timur's wives—of whom there were many—so we do not know who were the mothers of his children. The beautiful Mongol Princess Mulk-Hakun, Timur's oldest wife, better known as Bibi-Hanum, was childless and who Shah-Rukh's mother was is unknown.

Only a very thorough examination of the bones could help to solve the problem whether Timur was Shah-Rukh's real father. What complicated the task was that the two men belonged to two quite different racial types. Timur was a Mongoloid and Shah-Rukh a Europoid. Very clearly marked features of the Europoid type were recognisable even in details and Shah-Rukh's appearance must have been very like that of the present-day Tadjika. He must have inherited most of his features from his mother.

However, a very close examination of the skulls of both Timur and Shah-Rukh did provide indications of blood-relationship. Despite notable differences in skull measurements (indicating racial peculiarities) there were revealed quite clearly points in common, especially a similar asymmetry of the skull surfaces. This likeness arose from one and the same pathological condition. The same irregular deformation of the coronal suture resulted in both men displaying a left-sided so-called plagiocephaly. Such a resemblance could only be due to heredity.

In fact the broad, Mongoloid skull of Timur and the narrow, rather delicate Europoid skull of Shah-Rukh display a considerable number of physiognomical features in common which could only be attributed to blood-relationship. For instance a similar degree of asymmetry can clearly be seen in the piriform nasal opening although the formation of the nasal bones is quite different in the two skulls. Despite this the contour lines of the nasal bones do show a resemblance. The unmistakable likeness in the shape of the nose-forehead suture could hardly have been due to chance.

If these slight details play no part in the determination of race from the anthropological point of view, they do have great importance from the light they throw on the problem of blood-relationship. Neither the nuances in the delineation of the sutures, nor the general asymmetry of the skull, nor least of all the pathological peculiarities, can be due to chance. Such details can only arise from blood-relationship. So the question as to whether Timur was or was not the father of Shah-Rukh can be regarded as answered.

Shah-Rukh's whole skeleton gave an impression of delicacy. It was noticeable that under the influence of senile deformations there was a marked development of osteophytes on the vertebrae.

During the reconstruction of the face, the normal measurements of the thickness of the soft parts was made along the median line of the head. The refinement of the cheek-bones, the atrophy of the jaw-bones, taken together with the considerable density of structure of the whole facial skeleton, indicated a great senile desiccation. The nasal bones were so characteristic that the reconstruction of the nose presented no especial difficulties. The wings of the nose were judged to be thin, expanded and sharply defined.

The shape of the base of the skull and the projection of the mouth as it must have been in youth made it possible to reproduce the mouth in its senile deformation. The angles of the mouth had sunk, the whole width of the opening had become enlarged, the upper lip had sunk inwards and the lower lip had been pushed forwards.

Thanks to the conjunction of many peculiarities, the reconstitution of the ears could be undertaken on conclusive evidence. The relief of the small mastoid processes, the direction and the depth of the auditory meatus, the degree of development of the lower margin of the temporal bones, the direction of the ascending ramus of the lower jaw, furnished the necessary clues for representing the shape of the ears, their position and their degree of projection from the head. The distance between the middle of the eyebrows and the rim of the nasal opening determined the main measurements of the ears. The well-marked form of the wings of the nose afforded a basis for determining the relief of the ears. The senile weakening of the temporal muscles indicated a possible flabbiness of the upper part of the ear muscles.

The hair was reproduced from miniatures of the Timurid period since more exact information was lacking. The same evidence served for copying the head-covering and the clothing.

The work done on this skull provided a documentary portrait which was verified by evidence from contemporaries who described Shah-Rukh's appearance and character. In his youth he was an active, graceful and good-looking man, but by his sixtieth year he had retained nothing of his former good looks. Selfishness, cruelty and fanaticism, the main characteristics of this youngest son of Timur, had left their imprint.

Ulugh-Beg

Ulugh-Beg (1394–1449), grandson of Timur and son of Shah-Rukh, was an outstanding astronomer and the founder of an observatory which was regarded as the most perfected, admirably equipped and richly furnished of its time. Ulugh-Beg produced a map of the heavens and a table indicating the movements of the planets.

Ulugh-Beg, was buried at his grandfather's feet and under a slab similar to others of the dynasty but that covering Ulugh-Beg's remains was of rather coarse-grained grey marble carefully worked and was more massive than that under which his father Shah-Rukh lay.

The inscription on the slab reads:

> 'This radiant grave, this renowned place of martyrdom, this sweetly scented garden, this unattainable tomb is the last resting-place of the Ruler whose presence refreshes the gardens of paradise and gives joy to the paradisical regions, even of the beneficent Sultan, the learned Caliph who promoted peace and faith, Ulugh-Beg Sultan—may Allah shed light upon his grave! —whose happy birth occurred in the year 796 at the town of Sultania; in the month sil-Hidsha of the year 810 was he in the City of Security Samarkand, sovereign in his office of governor, he bowed himself only to the will of Allah—"each one swims as the time is apportioned to him"—when his life came to an end and when the appointed time that pitiless fate had determined, arrived, his son transgressed the law in that he struck his father with a dagger's point so that he found a martyr's death in the wilderness, so that he was removed to the House of Pity of his all-merciful Lord on 10th of Ramadan of the year 833 of the Hejira of the Prophet.'

During the opening of the grave the slab was raised by means of wedges and then into the space thus revealed was introduced a wire cable which gradually reached round the whole slab which was hoisted up some 6 inches by means of pulleys and then rolled aside on wooden cylinders.

The slab formed the cover of the sarcophagus whose sides were hewn from a solid block of marble. The bottom was composed of three closely joined slabs of grey marble like the rest of the tomb.

On the bottom lay the remains of Ulugh-Beg covered with a layer about 8 inches deep of fine chitin from crysalids of flies. The skeleton had upon it a delicate piece of woven stuff, apparently the remains of an unrolled turban. On the torso were fragments of a kind of shirt made of silk, which behind and on the sides were tucked into trousers of traditional Uzbek cut. Around the waist these were held in place with a broad, silk band ornamented with a checker pattern of white and light blue squares. The front of the shirt fell in a wide gusset almost to the knees.

The remains were, as is prescribed by the *Shariah,* laid on the back, the left shoulder raised on a little heap of earth. The head was also on a cushion of earth and portions of a reddish-coloured piece of stuff could be seen. The skull was by the side of the skeleton, at the height of the shoulders, its base upwards and the facial part turned towards the breast. Together with the skull there were in correct anatomical association the atlas, the epistropheus and part of the third neck vertebrae. On the vertebrae were clearly to be seen the marks made by a sharp instrument. Traces of cuts were also visible at the corners of the jaws. The lower jaw was in its right position next to the skull.

I examined the traces of cuts to determine how and with what weapon the head had been severed at one blow from the trunk. The blow could have been struck only by a man of immense strength and practical experience. The blade must have been drawn from side to side and not directly brought down. The murderer had seemingly stood above a kneeling victim. The scarcely perceptible vibrations in the cutting line through the vertebrae showed that the instrument used must have been very sharp and the blow very powerful. The weapon was probably an oriental sabre.

The chronicles and legends agree approximately in what they tell of the life and death of Ulugh-Beg. He was the eldest son of Shah-Rukh and was born on 22nd March 1394 at Sultania. His mother Gadhar Shad-Aga came of the noble race of the Jagatai and was the daughter of Gias-ed-Din-Tarchan whose ancestors—according to the historian Rashid-ed-Din—had saved the life of Jenghiz Khan. The noble origin and the wealth of Ulugh-Beg's maternal ancestors implied that the race existed in isolation and therefore presented a pure ethnical type. From all acounts Ulugh-Beg's mother was a typical Mongol of her time.

The child received the name of Mohammed-Torgai but this was soon dropped in favour of the nickname Ulugh-Beg which means literally 'Great Prince'. This name, a tribute to noble origin, was also appropriate to the young prince's character and behaviour.

When he was seventeen years of age he received from his grandfather Timur a huge apanage stretching from the Amur-Darya to Sisian in the north-west to Ankara in the north-east. In his youth

Ulugh-Beg often took part in his grandfather's campaigns. Later he was to gain a well-merited reputation as one of the most learned men of his time.

He was an accurate observer of the heavens and he drew up astronomical tables which even today are astonishing in their originality and precision. Ulugh-Beg built near Samarkand an observatory that was a treasure-house of oriental astronomy.

When Ulugh-Beg succeeded to the throne he was the leading learned man of central Asia. In the latter years of his reign religious quarrels flared up throughout his far-reaching dominions. There were bitter internecine struggles between numerous religious sects and they were marked with extreme fanaticism. So serious were these conflicts that Ulugh-Beg had to adopt severe measures of repression. The result was violent discontent among the clergy and this finally led to rebellion.

Exhausted by the prolonged struggle against enemies at home, spiritually depressed by having, against his own convictions, to proceed to unavoidable reprisals, Ulugh-Beg left Samarkand. Without any great armed force and with only a handful of faithful followers, he set out for Mecca.

Ulugh-Beg's son, Abulatif who wanted for himself the tottering throne of the ruler of Samarkand, was egged on by members of the religious sects to give his consent to patricide. Abulatif consented that one Abos, the son of a man who had been executed on Ulugh-Beg's orders, should avenge the supposedly innocent blood of his father. On a pitch-dark night when Ulugh-Beg, worn down by recent events and exhausted by a long, fatiguing journey, sat, plunged in sad thoughts, and sleepless by the camp-fire, Abos fell upon him, one of the tallest men of his day, forced him to his knees and with one blow of a sabre sliced off his head. In this tragic manner this outstanding scholar, astronomer and humanist was, by the will of his own son, murdered in his fifty-sixth year.

Only seldom can archaeologists get, as in this case, such irrefragable proof for the reliability of the statements of the chroniclers and of popular legends. The grave of Ulugh-Beg offered unimpeachable evidence for the tragedy of his death. According to the rules of the *Shariah* he was buried in the same clothing that he wore when he died. Indeed, if anyone suffered a violent death and was regarded as a *shadid,* that is a martyr, he must be buried in the clothes he was wearing when killed. He who met with death by violence (though not in battle) must, before burial, be neither undressed, or washed, and still less embalmed.

That Ulugh-Beg was interred in accordance with the ritual prescriptions is shown not only by the remains of his clothing but also by the innumerable fly chrysalids. For had the body been washed and reclothed the flies would not have appeared. Probably the corpse lay a fairly long time in the open air before it was found and buried according to the rites then prevailing.

The fragments of clothing were in a bad state of preservation. The rules of the *Shariah* forbade orthodox Moslems wearing silks next to the skin. Therefore such stuffs were woven from a mixture of silk and cotton, and from just such a material were made the shirt and the trousers of Ulugh-Beg, of which only a few silk fibres remained. The whole warp, however, was destroyed.

The position of Ulugh-Beg's bones showed clearly they had never been exhumed before. Although in a very imperfect condiion the textile could, however, be saved. V. I. Komonov, scientist and restorer at the State Hermitage in Leningrad, preserved the fabrics and then copied them for the museum.

The skeleton was in a good state, only the bones of the left elbow had been corroded by gypsum salts from some evaporation. Some traces of bone destruction due to the formation of gypsum could also be seen on the skull. The protuberances of the forehead, for instance, were slightly cracked. The remaining bones were, however, so well preserved that it was not necessary to treat them before removal.

I do not think I need give here any detailed anthropological description of Ulugh-Beg's skull. I will just confine myself to some statements without which the correctness of the portrait reconstruction cannot be checked.

The skull was in good condition and could be considered as complete save for the absence of almost all the teeth (lost in Ulugh-Beg's lifetime) and the portion of the lower jaw that was cut off during the murder. The skull viewed from the horizontal position showed an almost ovoid form. In section it was round, arched and the back of the head was not projecting. The slightly developed glabella was rendered somewhat more marked because of the smallness of the short supraorbital region. The face was ovoid, the eye-orbits were round and high. The long nasal bones were very narrow. The strongly developed point of the nose inclined almost imperceptibly downwards. The lower margin of the eye-sockets projected strongly so that the skull, taking into account the marked flattening of the cheek-bones, presented a Mongoloid character, although in general it was of Europoid type which he must have inherited from his father Shah-Rukh. Some features of the facial skeleton and of the skull were reminiscent, however, of his great ancestors.

Ulugh-Beg's delicate bodily form was like that of his father. He was not fat but of lean frame and thin in face and body.

Miran-Shah (1366–1407), a son of Timur

The reconstruction of Miran-Shah's outward appearance was rendered difficult since there was no certainty that the remains found in the Gur-i-Emir mausoleum really could be attributed to Miran-Shah. Various circumstances combined to arouse doubt in the minds of researchers. The death of Miran-Shah during a campaign, the transfer of his body from Tabriz to Samarkand, the secondary burial in the Gur-i-Emir mausoleum, the lack of an inscription on a slab over the grave and also the apparently right position of the skeleton.

Since there were no iconographic data, usual means of identification could not apply. The biographical material I had at my disposal was very scanty and did not allow me to form any clear idea of Miran-Shah's appearance.

Miran-Shah, Timur's third son, was born in 1366. The chronicles do not mention the name of his mother. He inherited from his father both courage and cruelty. When he was fourteen years of age he was already the ruler of Choresm and when he was thirty Timur appointed him governor of a huge area including Armenia, Georgia, Azerbaijan, Kurdistan, Irak Arabi and Irak Parsi (that is western Persia) and on his father's orders Miran-Shah also took part in some campaigns.

While he was out hunting in the autumn of 1396 he fell from his horse and as a result of this accident he began to give signs of mental disorder and a mania for destruction. Clavijo assures us that Miran-Shah destroyed one building just to get himself talked about: 'Mirsa Mironshah, without having created anything himself, had destroyed the most beautiful creation in the world.'

In the summer of 1397 Miran-Shah set out against Baghdad, then still in the hands of the Sultan Ahmed. But hardly had he got news of unrest among the population of Tabriz than he turned back and executed bloody reprisals on the rebels. In the autumn of that same year he waged another campaign when he caused frightful devastation. In the winter of 1397–8 more troubles broke out in Miran-Shah's apanage and they were suppressed with dreadful brutality. He had men hanged, monumental buildings razed and finally performed an act of quite inexplicable profanation on the body of the historian Rashid-ed-Din who was no contemporary of Miran-Shah but was executed in 1318, forty-eight years before the latter was born. There could have been then no personal reasons for this injury done to the memory of one of the leading historical writers of central Asia. But Miran-Shah had Rashid-ed-Din's corpse dug up and thrown into a Jewish cemetery.

The incredible cruelties, accompanied by a blind lust for destruction to which many of the most beautiful buildings in Tabriz were to be sacrificed, aroused rumours that Miran-Shah was mad. Information, however, about his mental state is extremely contradictory.

The historians Abd-er-Rezzok Samarkandi and Mirhond report Miran-Shah's cruelties, Daulet-Shah (a fifteenth-century biographer of poets) on the other hand recounts that Miran-Shah was straightforward, mild and a patron of the arts. Among others he was the patron of the Persian poet Kemal Hodshendi who lived in Tabriz from 1393 to 1403. According to Daulet-Shah, Miran-Shah was a frequent visitor to the poet's house. Once the poet and his lord were so deep in conversation that they did not notice Miran-Shah's pages had quite stripped an apricot tree in the garden. When Miran-Shah heard that all the fruit from the garden was to pay the poet's debts, he awarded him a sum of

10,000 dinars which was far more than the value of the crop. Such are the contradictions to be found in the accounts of the chroniclers.

The Armenian historian Tavma (Thomas) of Mezop calls Miran-Shah 'a very gracious ruler with a mild character' and mentions especially that he showed toleration towards Christians.

It may therefore be quite possible that Miran-Shah's cruelty was not caused by mental derangement but was a reaction excited by the hostility of the Tabriz inhabitants towards the Timurids. Miran-Shah was particularly hated by the extreme Hurifi sect of the Shi'-ites since in 1401 or 1402 Fadlallah, the founder and patron saint of the sect, had been put to death on Miran-Shah's orders and Miran-Shah was stigmatised as Antichrist (Od-Dadshal) and as King of the Serpents (Marham-Shah).

Sevin-Beg, a grand-daughter of Khan Uzbek, was married to Miran-Shah's elder brother Jehangir and their son Mohammed Sultan was Timur's favourite grandson. After Jehangir's death Sevin-Beg, according to ancient custom, became the wife of her brother-in-law Miran-Shah. The written records tell of the unbelievable jealousy and brutality she had to suffer from until at last she was forced to flee and seek refuge at the court of her mighty father-in-law, Timur himself.

The constant troubles, and the ruthlessness with which Miran-Shah suppressed them, spread ruin in the territories ruled by him and no doubt induced Timur in 1399 to remove him from his governorships. But from letters addressed by Shah-Rukh it would seem that Miran-Shah retained the lordship over Arron (between the lower course of the Kura and the Arash), Mugan and Armenia and also was nominal ruler of Georgia.

At about this time Clavijo saw Miran-Shah in Sultania and did not get the impression he was mentally deranged. At least nothing in the Timurid's appearance indicated madness—Clavijo also reports that at this period Miran-Shah complained of pains in his feet.

After Timur's death, Miran-Shah joined with his son Abu-Beg in war against another son, Omar. The feud went on uninterruptedly for many months until in 1408 Kara-Yusuf, the chief of nomadic Turkomen tribes, together with Sultan Ahmed defeated Miran-Shah's army in southern Azerbaijan and Miran-Shah himself fell in the battle. The Turkoman chief, who had no idea that it was Miran-Shah who had been killed, plundered his belongings, stripped his body and finally slashed off his head with a knife.

The death of Miran-Shah was related in some detail by the German adventurer Johann Schildtberger who fought on the side of the Crusaders at Nicopolis in 1396 and was taken prisoner by the Osmanli Turks. When in 1402 Timur crushed the Turks near Ankara, among the prisoners he took was Schildtberger, and he was with Miran-Shah's army when it was defeated. The description given by Schildtberger agrees, generally speaking, with the accounts of the Persian authors. According to the German's story, when Kara-Yusuf had cut off Miran-Shah's head he had it impaled and set up before the walls of Tabriz so as to induce the inhabitants to surrender the city. Shortly afterwards he sent the head and body of Miran-Shah to his brother at Samarkand—with apologies!

How long the dervish, who was to take Miran-Shah's remains to Samarkand, spent on his journey, we do not know. There is also no information as to the date when the body was finally interred in the Gur-i-Emir mausoleum.

There was no agreement among experts on central Asian history as to whether the bones which were discovered really belonged to Miran-Shah. Professor M. J. Masson and A. Y. Yakubowski, a corrresponding member of the Academy of Sciences, authorities on the epoch of the Timurids, doubted the authenticity of the skeleton on the following grounds:

1 The circumstances alone of Miran-Shah's death (the headless and stripped body) allows one to suppose a number of possibilities including a substitution of the body.
2 The traditional dynastic slab did not exist over the grave that was opened.
3 The almost correct and undisturbed position of the skeletal bones was suspicious since we know the body was brought to Samarkand by a dervish and it is very unlikely the remains were quite uninjured during the journey.

With all due respect to the arguments of the scientists I cannot agree with them. I will endeavour, as well as I can, to prove the opposite and will justify my proof exclusively by the osteological material.

First of all I should like to remind my readers that none of the Timurid burials in the Gur-i-Emir mausoleum was primary, that is to say all the bodies had been interred elsewhere before the remains were transferred to the mausoleum. Not only the body of Miran-Shah but also that of Shah-Rukh took a long road from Herat to Samarkand. The remains of the latter were, moreover, carried with him by his son Ulugh-Beg in the difficult circumstances of a retreat after a lost battle. The correct anatomical arrangement of Shah-Rukh's bones has, however, not called forth any doubt as to their authenticity from scientists.

But a careful examination of Miran-Shah's bones pointed to the conclusion that they had undoubtedly been secondarily interred. The main skeleton—as was at once obvious—showed the bones in correct anatomical association. The skull with the closely adjacent lower jaw lay on the right cheek-bone, away from the neck vertebrae which were in the natural order although they were turned round backwards. Some finger-bones lay near the feet. Both heel- and ankle-bones were in proper anatomical association with each other and with the bones of the leg.

For this state of things there was only one explanation. Kara-Yusuf, as historical students have also pointed out, certainly made good use of Miran-Shah's haphazard death. The head of their cruel master set up before the walls of Tabriz undoubtedly led to the surrender of the town. But then Kara-Yusuf the Turkoman, fearing the wrath of Shah-Rukh, had sent his brother's remains to Samarkand.

It is also certain that Miran-Shah's body was at least partially mummified.

I do not know what mummification technique was used. Probably the body was first of all desiccated in order to prevent signs of decomposition and then certainly treated with colophonium, camphor and some disinfecting substance unknown to me.

In this connection perhaps one may mention that when Timur's grave was opened, an intoxicating odour of resinous substances, an odour bitter-sweet and resembling the scent of incense and camphor, was wafted up to us. For several days after the opening of the grave the perfume still could be noticed. V. V. Komonov inclines to the opinion that the odour came from a product of decomposition of crystallised camphor, benzoin, and other resins he could not identify.

It is obvious then that Miran-Shah's remains were mummified. The desiccation of the neck muscles led to their contraction which had as a result an unnatural compression of the neck vertebrae. As was usual at the period Miran-Shah's body would have been sewn up in hides. The head was presumably packed apart. Contemporaries relate that it was presented to Shah-Rukh at Samarkand.

The dervish passed many days on his journey before he got to Samarkand with Miran-Shah's remains. On the way the body was still more desiccated and despite special precautions some parts of the mummy were broken off. The fingers and both feet were damaged but the detached bones were diligently gathered together and interred.

From all this it appears that the correct anatomical association of the skeleton can in no way be taken as a proof of its inauthenticity. Also the facts about Miran-Shah's death and the circumstances that he was interred twice in no way contradict the impression we got at the opening of the grave. Still, that was not enough to enable us to refer the skeleton with absolute certainty to Miran-Shah.

At this point I want to make some remarks of an archaeological-criminological kind which may lead to an answer to the questions of some sceptical inquirers.

In the upper hall of the Gur-i-Emir mausoleum there are placed several decorative gravestones within a space surrounded by a marble open-work barrier. In the middle of this space is the famous dark-green nephrite tomb. Round Timur's monument were arranged the other tombs in a definite order. The tombs above in the main hall occupy positions exactly corresponding to those of the actual graves below in the crypt. Above the grave attributed to Miran-Shah, was a slab indicating that it was the burial-place of Miran-Shah, son of the Emir Timir.

The sceptical may object that the upper hall of the Gur-i-Emir mausoleum was, long before the excavations of the year 1941, restored by Viatkin and Barthold, and that during the restoration certain errors may have been made and faults committed.

There is, however, reliable evidence that the work of restoration was carried out with care. Each of the inscribed slabs has its own particular size and Viatkin laid them down exactly each in its own place as indicated by the marks of the mortar on the floor of the hall.

I opened the grave with an inscription marking it as Miran-Shah's.

During the removal of the gravestone it was evident that only the upper part of the grave was of later date than the burial. Part of the covering over the grave had been destroyed, the vault had sunk and the actual burial chamber was two-thirds filled with earth and rubble. The grave was a rectangular space cut down into the earth. Its floor and sides were roughly plastered. The skeleton lay directly on the bottom and had been interred, to all appearances, without any coffin. The left side of the remains was pushed up close to the grave's wall. The left shoulder was slightly raised. Obviously, as prescribed by the Shariah earth had been sprinkled among the bones.

The free circulation of ground waters which had seeped through the thin layer of plaster had hastened the destruction of organic tissue. Of clothing, skin, hair or muscles no trace was to be seen. The bones were in a poor state of preservation and the cranium had broken into several fragments. Thanks to the measures taken for preserving the bones and to the care taken in their recovery, these were undamaged.

Closer examination of the skull showed that all the facial region was well preserved and even the delicate nasal bones were undamaged. When the skull fragments were joined together there appeared defects in both temporal bones. Deep cracks radiating from the middle of the skull vault had partially accelerated the destruction of the parietal bones in their median region. The frontal bone, the occipital bone and both temporals were quite intact. With the skull in this condition the destruction of the parietals appeared all the more striking. The historical accounts, however, which we have of Miran-Shah's death throw some light on what seems apparently inexplicable.

Many teeth were missing from both jaws, but from the good condition of the sockets these seem to have been lost after Miran-Shah's death. Besides these defects the skull also showed further damage worth a special mention. The damage to the skull showed clearly that the head had been severed from the trunk by a powerful blow with a dagger delivered from the side.

The defects on the inner surface of the foramen magnum were also very revealing—four cruciform indentations with smooth surfaces. Such damage to the bone is possible only if the head is impaled on a point with a lozenge-shaped cross-section. The condition of the skull indicated very clearly that what the chroniclers and historians recount about Miran-Shah's death is reliable.

All this strengthened us in the opinion that the remains must undoubtedly be those of Miran-Shah.

The clearly marked cranial sutures and the recently completed formation of the base, taken together with the degree of wear of the teeth, indicated that Miran-Shah was about forty years old when he was killed.

The ethnical type of the skull cannot be described in a very few words. The Europoid and Mongoloid features were so intermingled that it is difficult to assign the preponderance to the one or the other. Such mixed types are common among the recent Uzbeks and Tadjiks. If we compare together all the skulls in the Gur-i-Emir mausoleum the resemblance of this skull, ascribed to Miran-Shah, to that of Shah-Rukh appears obvious. The same narrow face, the same thin, strongly projecting nose, the quite characteristic profile, the deep jaw fossae and the high, rounded eye-orbits.

On the horizontal plane Miran-Shah's skull occupies a place about midway between the spheroidal and the sphenoidal. The marked deformation during Miran-Shah's lifetime was connected morphologically with the irregular growth of the coronal suture. This typical appearance of so-called left-sided plagiocephaly, due to pathological hypertrophy of the skull, was more marked in Miran-Shah than in the progenitor of the Timurids. The protuberances on the dome-shaped forehead were in astonishing contrast with the delicate facial skeleton. The bones of the vault with its slightly marked interior cranial relief would indicate a secondary ossification of the skull vault owing to pathological conditions. The skull was large, but light, the bones of the vault uncommonly delicate and soft and the whole somewhat effeminate and smooth. The superciliary ridges were very slightly developed and short, the face was asymmetrical and apparently developed towards the right, but its general contour could be called ovoid. The eye-sockets were high but relatively small, the cheek-bones were pronounced. The root of the nose was high, the lengthy nasal bones curved. The comparatively broad upper jaw was prognathous, the lower jaw weak with delicate, narrow rami, light body and slightly developed, hardly projecting chin. It could be seen that in both jaws the incisors were prognathous, the teeth on the whole were scarcely worn down at all—neither were there traces of decay.

The extraordinary delicacy of the facial skeleton was noteworthy which undoubtedly indicated a pathological condition and was clearly of the same origin as the hypertrophy of the skull. So it is clear that such a skull must have belonged to a pathological individual, whose afflictions were very probably connected with symptoms of a disordered brain.

The hypertrophic broadening of the skull vault had among other consequences resulted in a reduction of the temporal fossa which in its turn led to a weakening of the temporal muscles.

The formation of the eye-sockets and the marked projection of their lower margin suggests a considerable bulginess of the eyes themselves such as often occurs in feeble-minded subjects or sufferers from Basedow's disease. In fact the condition of Miran-Shah's skull strengthens the evidence of the historians concerning his morbid temperament.

Clavijo mentioned that Miran-Shah suffered from pains in his feet. In both the feet of the skeleton were traces of a pathological condition which might well cause pain.

Since Miran-Shah's skull presented just the same pathological change in the vault as did all the other Timurid skulls, we can conclude that the skeleton from the Gur-i-Emir grave without a dynastic slab really belonged to Miran-Shah. The reconstructed portrait from the skull also showed the blood-relationship between Miran-Shah and Timur and also that Shah-Rukh and Miran-Shah were brothers in the full blood. They inherited their Europoid features from their mother, by birth a Tadjik.

The gradual modification of the physical type of the Timurids also shows how recent has been the formation of the Uzbek ethnical type—it originated from a mixture of the Europoid Pamir-Ferghana type with immigrant Turkish-Mongoloid strains shortly before the beginning of the Timurid dynasty which was about two centuries before the formation of the Uzbek state in the seventeenth century.

Admiral Ushakov

Feodor Feodorovich Ushakov (1744–1817) was an eminent Russian naval commander and one of the founders of the Russian naval tradition. Under him the Russian Fleet was victorious at Fidonissi (1788), in the Kerch Strait (1790) and in the Mediterranean (1798–1800). The capture of the fortress of Korf, the liberation of Naples and other Italian towns are also linked with the name of Ushakov. In his memory The Presidium of the Supreme Soviet of the U.S.S.R. founded on 3rd March 1944 the Ushakov Order (first and second class), together with a Ushakov medal.

On 18th August 1944, on the instructions of the People's Commissar for the Navy ('People's Commissar' was the name then given to ministers) a special commission was appointed to search for Ushakov's grave. From various historical documents it would appear that between the town of Temnikov and the Sanaksary monastery (Mordvin Autonomous Socialist Soviet Republic) the Ushakovs once possessed a small family property.

It so happened that through intrigues at the Court of Alexander 1st Feodor Ushakov, one of the remarkable statesmen of his time, an experienced diplomatist and a talented naval commander, was forced into retirement and had to end his days on his remote estate. But even before the admiral's death his glorious victories in the Mediterranean—which must be accounted among the most famous exploits in the history of the Russian Fleet—had fallen into oblivion.

Feodor Ushakov died in 1817 aged seventy-three and his mortal remains were laid to rest in the grounds of the Sanaksary monastery. Later on a marble monument was raised over the grave and close by a chapel. In 1916 the monument with the monastery in the background was photographed and this picture facilitated the search for the admiral's grave, since when the commission began its work no traces of either monument or chapel could be seen.

The excavations were made to include the site of the former chapel. At a depth of 70 centimetres (about 2 feet 4 inches) lay parts of a building and rubble. Directly under the floor of this former building was discovered, 1½ metres down, the crumbled roof of a single brick vault. The vault was badly damaged, the coffin and the remains it contained were no longer in their original position.

After the excavation work was finished it could be ascertained that the remains must certainly be those of Admiral Ushakov. There were remnants of a uniform dating from the time of Alexander 1st and the gold trimming from the collar, and the cuffs, as well as the epaulettes with three black eagles on a golden ground, were preserved. Obviously the bones were those of Ushakov.

The skeleton was in a poor condition. Only the skull was still well preserved and it was evident at a first glance that the portrait of Ushakov executed from life did not show much resemblance to the real visage of the admiral. Therefore the commission asked for a portrait-document of Ushakov to be prepared.

The skull was sphenoid on the horizontal plane, in cross-section sub-brachycephalous with a rounded vault. The hinder part of the head was rather projecting but the occipital torus was not strongly developed. The supraorbital region was only slightly marked, the glabella appeared to be prominent only in contrast to the steep forehead and the deeply situated root of the nose. The broad face was short, the eye-orbits had an irregular rounded form.

The nasal aperture, with thin margins, was pear-shaped, the sub-nasal margin and the anterior point of the nose that projected only slightly, were sharply delineated. The nasal bones were very short and seen in profile, curved. The alveolar process was short and wide and almost all the teeth were missing.

The rather flat face had broad cheek-bones. The lower jaw was distorted through obliteration though it was very massive with steep ascending rami and a strongly projecting chin.

The following experiment indicated to what an extent the skull differed from the painted portrait. A careful drawing of the skull in the same position as the head in the portrait was prepared and thus the distortion of the real face displayed. The skull proved to be both shorter and wider than the face of the painting.

In the Russia of Alexandrian times fashion favoured the so-called 'canon of David' according to which artists must purposely lengthen the faces of their models in order to make the features look more aristocratic and noble. But all the same the artists endeavoured to preserve the individuality of their sitters. Thus various details agreed well enough whereas the skull and the painted portrait did not at all correspond in the main measurements. Still, it must be assumed that the portrait really was painted from nature. Also the documentary portrait I prepared corresponded to the conclusions of the facial experts concerning the outward appearance of the admiral.

After our work was done the skull was once more interred at the Sanaksary monastery. The reproductions of the head are in the Moscow Historical Museum and in the Naval Museum at Leningrad.

The Scythian King Skiluros

Skiluros, one of the most famous of the Scythian rulers, lived in the second century B.C. and during his reign coins bearing his image and superscription were struck at Olbia.

The monumental mausoleum adjoining the city walls of the Scythian Neapolis was one of the most remarkable discoveries made by the Taurida-Scythian expedition led by the archaeologist P. N. Schulz. The mausoleum contained more than seventy graves with the remains of men, women and children of various ages. The building abutted on the southern wall of the city and its mighty walls were formed of square stone blocks cemented together and probably painted, as pieces of plaster with traces of red and yellow pigment indicate. The brick covering was probably in the form of a tent and was supported on a wooden framework. The entrance was in the eastern wall where were the remains of a wooden door. The earthern floor was covered with a level layer of white plaster.

The expedition also came across the skeletons of four horses in the main part of the mausoleum. Most of the human bones were in rectangular pinewood coffins but one skeleton of a female lay in a finely carved wooden sarcophagus. The most ancient burial was in the north-west corner. This tomb was of well-hewn white limestone slabs and was set into a rectangular depression cut down into the rock. The peculiar features of this tomb's construction pointed indeed to the most ancient interment and it was apparently for this grave that the mausoleum was erected in the first place. All the other burials were undoubtedly of later date, probably at the end of the second century B.C., but some possibly in the first century B.C.

In the stone sepulchre lay the undisturbed remains of a man.

The skeleton lay stretched out on its back. The head was turned towards the west. The right arm was bent. At the feet the man's armature was buried with him—an iron helmet, two swords, three spear-heads and against the left hip the remains of a quiver with applied gold ornamentation. The belt was fastened with a buckle and hook on which animal forms were represented. The designs were executed in the traditional 'animalistic' style. The quiver contained typical Scythian triangular iron arrow-heads. At the same spot were also found some 800 rather small ornaments of fine gold-foil and of Bosporus-Greek and Scythian origin.

The monumental tomb, the rich armour and the splendour of the robes pointed to the grave as having been that of a Scythian king. Judging by the objects found, the interment as well as the mausoleum itself could be dated to the second century B.C.

Although in the mausoleum about seventy skeletons were

discovered, the remaining craniological material was in a condition that left much to be desired. Before G. F. Debez received the bones for anthropological examination, they were partly restored by us and consolidated. During the provisional preservation of the skulls I noticed that they were, for the most part, in their main features, thoroughly Europoid and the male skulls in general resembled those of the Scyths of the Black Sea steppes. But among these skulls from the mausoleum were some with very delicate, narrow face, thin strongly prominent noses, as well as types with flattened faces, broad noses and Negroid traits. There were no skulls of a definite Mongoloid type. All this was just my first impression since at this stage of our work we had not undertaken any precise measurements.

G. F. Debez, however, who closely examined the skulls of this series, concluded that the anthropological types in this mausoleum of Scythian Neapolis showed strong racial admixture.

At the request of P. N. Schulz I undertook the reconstruction of the skull from the main tomb. The skull was massive, dolichocephalic with a slightly (no doubt artificially) deformed vault. The forehead was narrow and flattened. The eye-orbits and part of the frontal bone seem to have been displaced by deformation and this further strengthened the impression of a remarkably large development of the region above the eyes.

The orbits were not large, of medium height, the projecting cheek-bones rather high, massive, of simple pattern and somewhat flattened—yet none of these features reminded one of the Mongoloid type. The shape of the cheek-bones indeed resembled much more that of the ancient Cro-Magnon type, with strongly projecting nose but small nasal opening. The point of the nasal bones was stout, the alveolar process was not large and, compared with the skull measurements, narrow. The teeth in both jaws were small and in the upper jaw slightly projecting. The lower jaw was very heavy and massive, especially the chin.

To determine the age of the individual at death was very difficult. The obliteration of the coronal suture appeared to indicate an age of about fifty.

The reproduction showed the head of a strong, robust man. The peculiar formation of the cheek-bones determined the shape

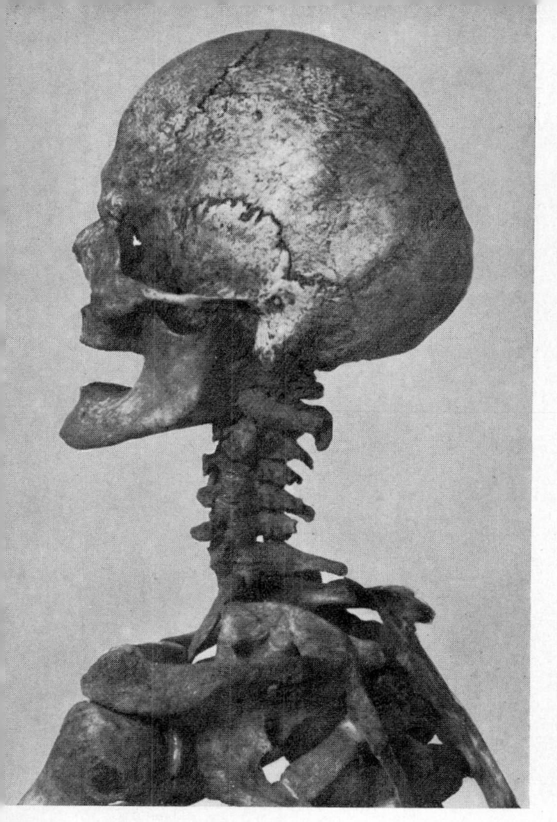

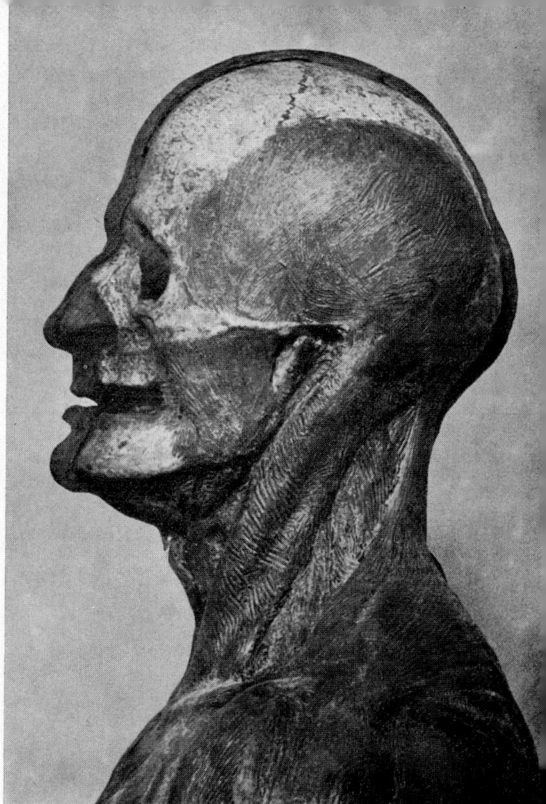

Rudagi the poet died in the year 941 and for more than a thousand years his grave had been searched for. (*Above left*) Rudagi's mounted skeleton. The complete absence of teeth can clearly be seen. The head is inclined backwards, and the nuchal part of the backbone strongly bent. (*Above right*) The masticatory, neck and chest muscles reconstructed. (*Below*) The portrait of Rudagi reconstructed from the skull.

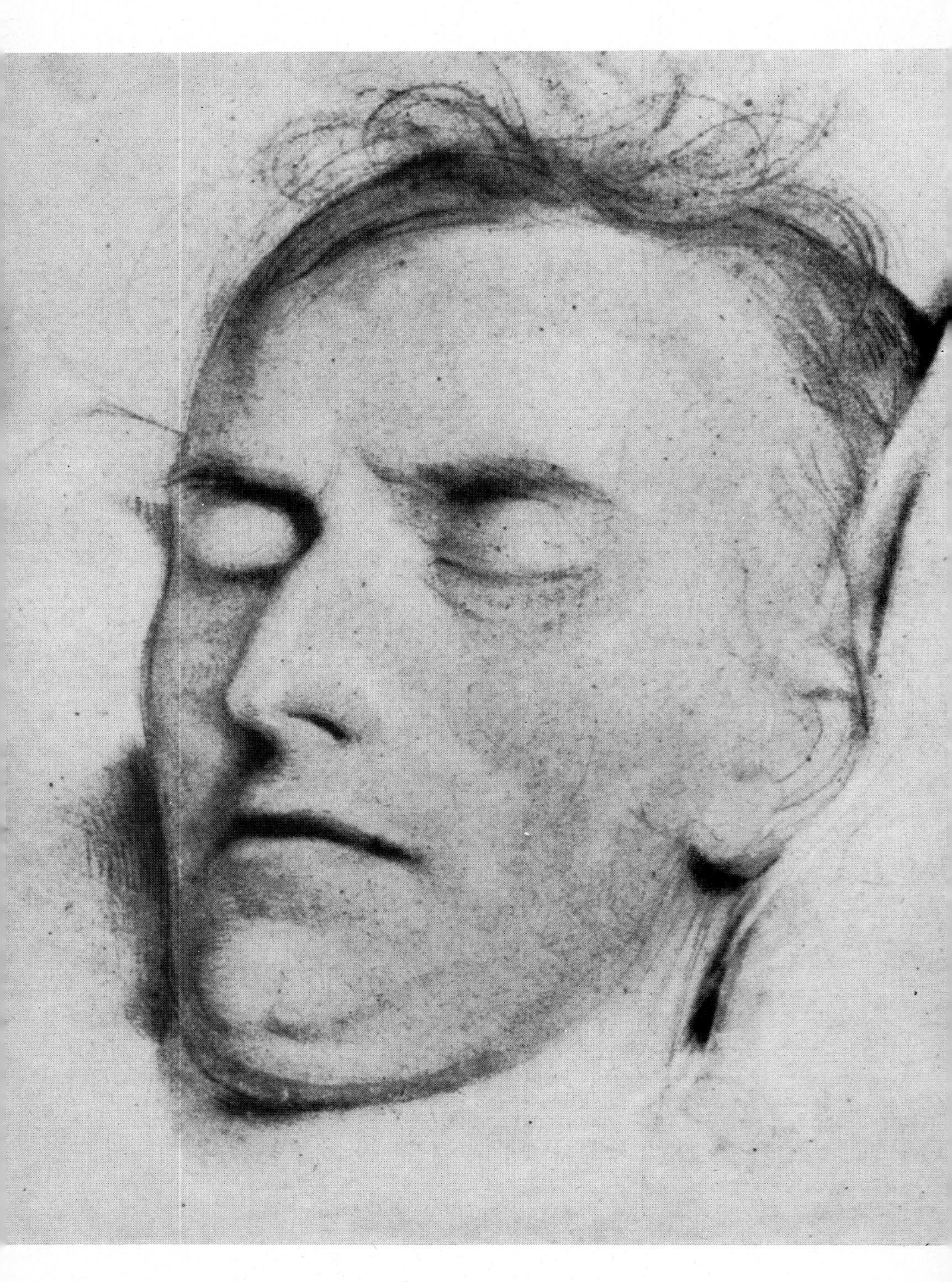

Schiller on his death-bed (from a drawing by Professor Jagelmann).

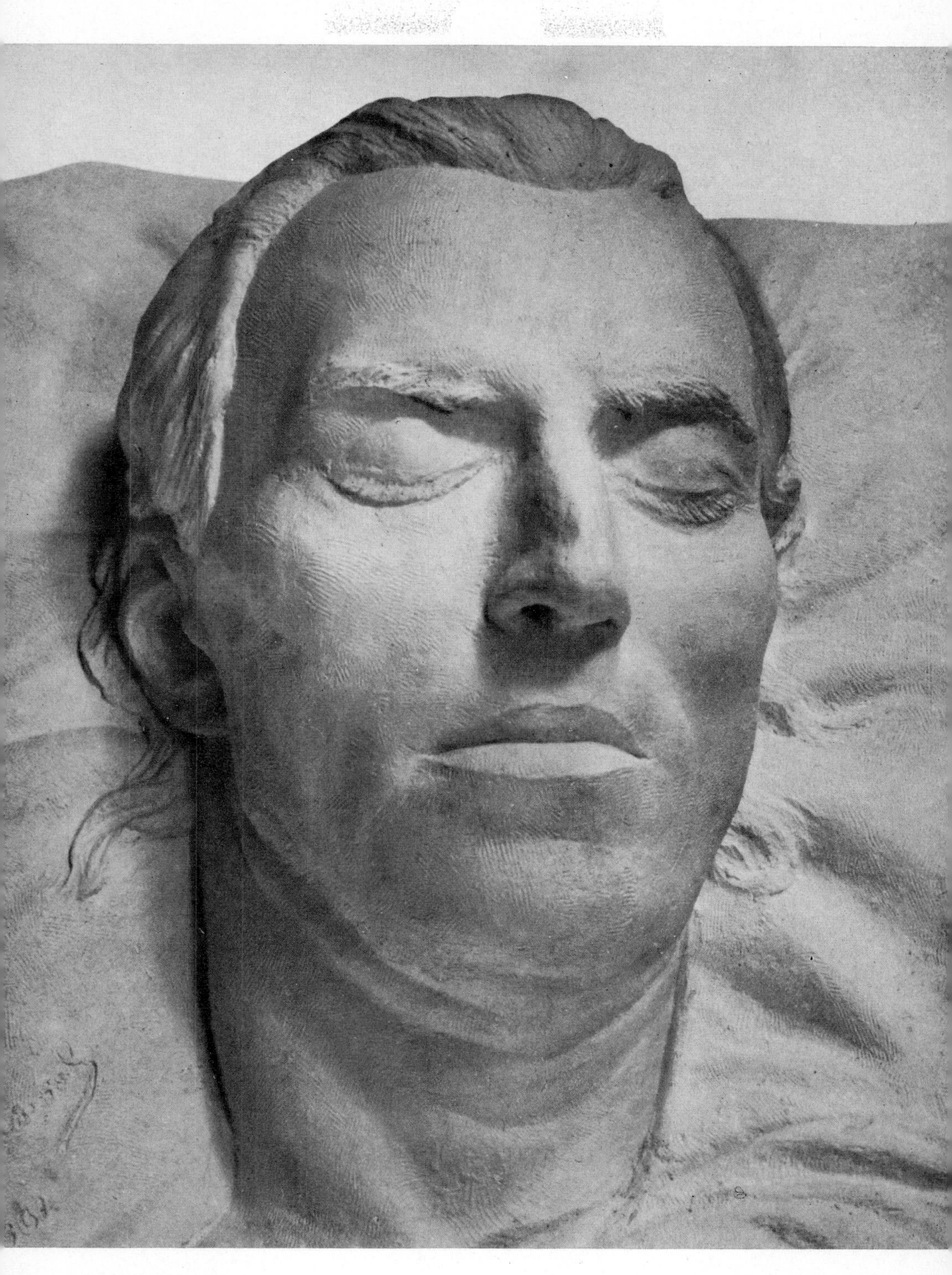

The author's reconstructed portrait of the dead Schiller. A radiant visage with closed eyes and a faint smile on the lips.

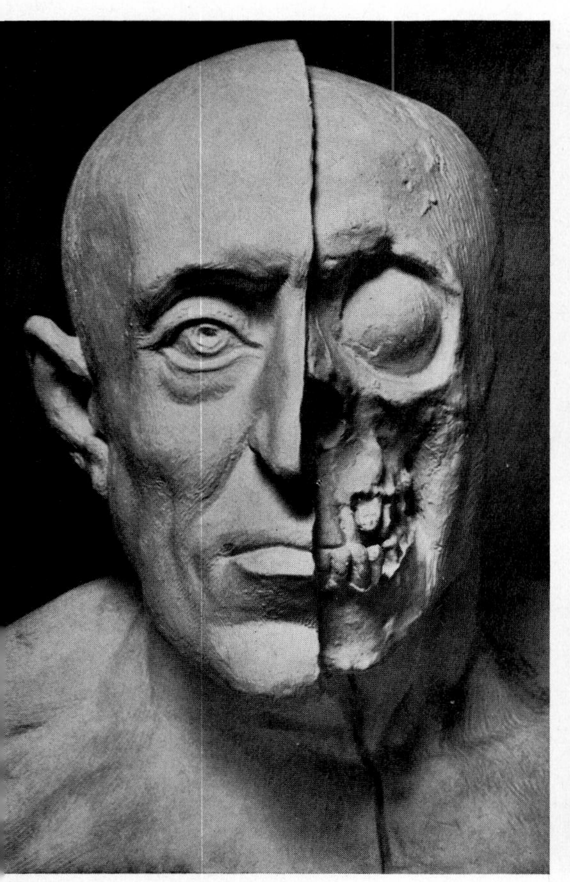

(*Left*) A phase of the reconstruction of the portrait of Ivan the Terrible. (*Right*) The complete reconstitution – a drooping nose and a projecting lower lip. The Tsar's expression was harsh, commanding and cruel. The mouth's contemptuous drawn-down corners expressed disgust and abhorrence; in all its details the face corresponded to what Ivan's contemporaries related of him.

of the cheeks. These, taken in conjunction with the finely contoured, small mouth, gave the impression of a very youthful face, an impression that was not modified even by the heavy folds of the upper eyelids.

For exhibition in the museum the portrait-reconstruction had to be completed by a typical Scythian arrangement of the long hair of the beard and the head. For indications we turned to the representation of a Scythian on a silver vessel from Voronesh. The impression was surprising. The carving presented characteristics very similar to those of the Scythian king Skiluros in the second century B.C.

For many years Schulz had worked on the identification of portraits of the Scythian king, several of which are known. In 1827 the archaeologist Darember discovered near the village of Kremenchik several bas-reliefs and the pedestal of a statue on which the names of King Skiluros and his son Palak were mentioned. Several coins from Olbia bearing Skiluros portraits are also known. P. N. Schulz proved that the site of Kremenchik lay within the territory of the old Scythian town of Neapolis and that the bas-reliefs in question really did depict Skiluros and Palak. According to Poseidonius Skiluros had fifty sons and Appollonidos even mentions eighty.

The portraits show Skiluros with a long beard, therefore Schulz was confirmed in his opinion that Skiluros died at an advanced age. As the age of the warrior was set at fifty, Schulz did not think of identifying him with the Scythian ruler, although the dating fully corresponded with that of Skiluros's lifetime.

However, when Schulz looked at the portrait-reconstruction, there suddenly flashed through his mind 'Must not that be Skiluros?' Without asking my opinion he just suggested I compare various Scythian pictures with the portrait of the warrior. Soon afterwards I received a dozen photographs of Scythian objects showing portraits . . . from among the lot I chose four which clearly depicted one and the same person and which bore a resemblance to the head I had reconstructed. As it turned out later all four portraits were known to be of King Skiluros—the first was on a fragment of a bas-relief from Kremenchik and the other three were enlargements of coins from Olbia. The coins were struck at various times and from various dies but they all bore on the reverse the name of Skiluros.

The unquestionable similarity between the reconstructed head and the representations made at various dates justified the identification of the reconstructed head with that of Skiluros, especially as the portraits were recognisable, by specific individual traits, as of one and the same person.

As I have mentioned, the skull bore traces of artificially produced deformation which had also influenced some other details of the facial skeleton. Hence the reconstructed head displayed peculiarities in the form of the nose, cheeks and forehead which greatly resembled those in the ancient, undoubtedly authentic, portraits of King Skiluros.

Rudagi (Rudaki)

Farid-ed-din Mohammed Abdullah Rudagi, Tadjik poet, was born about the middle of the ninth century and died in 941. He was the founder of Tadjik literature and was famed for his *kasidas* and *ghazzals*. His poems are distinguished by great literary mastery.[1]

In 1939 I gave a lecture at the Moscow Scientists' Club. My subject was the reconstitution of the face from the skull. When I had finished Sadriddin, a Tadjik scientist and writer, came up to me and expressed great interest in my work.

'What a great pity,' he said, 'that you will not be able to handle the bones of the most illustrious man of our culture. How pleased I should be to have from you a portrait of the founder of Persian-Tadjik classical poetry, Rudagi. Unfortunately his burial-place is unknown.'

'Can you, an expert on the history of your people, give no reliable statement about Rudagi's grave?'

Sadriddin Aini did not leave my question quite unanswered since in the following year (1940) he published an essay entitled

[1] Rudagi (or Rudaki) is generally in the West accounted a Persian poet since the language he wrote in was medieval Persian but his home was in what is now the Soviet Republic of Tadjikistan. The language of the Tadjiks is moreover closely akin to Persian.

'Rudagi's Grave and the village of Rudag'. But the search for the poet's last resting-place proved fruitless. . . .

Seventeen years had passed since my meeting with Sadriddin Aini when, out of the blue, in August 1956, I got a letter from Duschaube. The organising committee for the festivities planned to celebrate the 1100th birthday of the poet, invited me to undertake excavations to discover Rudagi's grave.

On 18th November 1956 I was in Duschaube where I was informed that Aini had managed to decipher an ancient MS by Sam'ami, a twelfth-century historical writer. In this document occurred this passage: 'Thus spoke Abusaid Idrisi Hafiz. "Known is it that the grave of Abdullah Rudagi lies behind the garden of Banji Rudag. Men visit it and I also tarried by this grave." ' Since Abusaid Idrisi (who also wrote a history of Samarkand) flourished in the tenth century he was almost a contemporary of the poet and died only some sixty years after Rudagi. His account then may be regarded as quite reliable.

A. A. Semenov, member of the Tadjikistan Academy of Science, told me that as early as 1939 he had openly expressed the opinion that Rudagi must have been buried at Kishlak Rudag, his little home town, somewhere in the neighbourhood of Samarkand, but just where this mountain village lay, he could not say.

Semenov was also of the opinion that Aini had undoubtedly been right in identifying the ancient name of the village Banji Rudak (Arabic) with that of the present-day Panji-Rudak (or Panjrud for short), that is in Tadjik 'Five Streams'. He added that the search had not yet been successful, but mentioned that at one time a monumental tomb, a so-called *Mazar*, had been erected over the grave. So it was certainly worth while to look for the poet's remains.

The village of Panjrud was a very ancient place of settlement and therefore several graveyards might well have existed and in every ancient Moslem cemetery the remains of one or more *Mazars* can be found. In which graveyard lay the bones of Rudagi? Moreover, what proof would there be that any given grave sheltered what were really the remains of the poet? Often an inscribed gravestone will provide a clue, but then again it is well known that gravestones get changed over from one grave to another. But worst of all was that such a stone over Rudaki's burial-place had never existed!

Islamic graves of early times hardly ever contain any extraneous objects, or if they do then these objects are at most a vessel or rosary beads—and such things would hardly serve to identify Rudagi's bones. So, recourse must be had to individual peculiarities of the poet such as might still be found on his skeleton.

In many cases I had been able to establish parallels between written records and injuries or anomalies on the actual remains of the persons mentioned.

So it might be possible in the case of Rudagi to identify certain bodily changes which would be mentioned in the written records.

But neither historians nor literary researchers who had studied the sparse information about Rudagi could be of any help to me. We just knew that the poet was blind.

So what I had at my disposal were very scanty and even contradictory statements. The earliest mention of Rudagi comes from a twelfth-century source, the *Kitab-ul-Ansab* of As-Sam'ani.

It was thus on very little material that Sadriddin Aini had based his theory that Rudagi must have been buried in the village of Panjrud. In the twelfth-century literary source called *Luhah al-albah* it is mentioned that Rudagi was born blind. The information about the burial-place seemed likely to be reliable whereas the story about the poet having been born blind appeared considerably less credible.

However, this data was far from being sufficient to determine whether any skeleton we might discover could or could not be that of Rudagi. Moreover we should not leave out of account the statement of the local inhabitants about the poet's burial-place.

As it was I had only one untapped source—the actual works of the poet themselves. Experts had never examined Rudagi's poetry to discover the autobiographical material in it; this seemed to have been hidden beneath the expression of his figures and forms, the colour and splendour of his rhymes and the fire that sparkles from his words. But such autobiographical material might be found and might be of use in identifying the poet's bones.

According to legend Rudagi wrote 1,300,000 lines of verse of which only some hundreds have survived. Since it is not possible to present the poems in their original language, we will offer a literal translation which is quite enough to serve our purpose. What we want to do above all is to examine them closely regarding the congenital blindness of Rudagi.

Poem on Wine

Soon it acquires the colour of ruby and coral.
How much beauty of the Yemen agate is in it!
How many rubies of Badashan does it contain!
Soon thou gazeth on a spring blazing like the sun.
Thou beholdest the crystal vessel
And it is a red pearl in the hand of Moses Imrat.
Bring me wine that seems like pure ruby
Or glittering sword in the sunlight.
In its purity it seems in its glass like rose-water,
In comforting pleasure like sleep to the sleepless eye.

In view of such poetry how can one hold that its author was born blind? Only a man with sight could know how a sword glitters in the sunlight, only a man with sight could distinguish between the red of the ruby and that of the coral, between the colour of agate, of pearls and of rose-water. What shades of colour, what transparency, what splendour!

Lightning rips like a sword through the clouds
From afar on the fields laugh the tulips.
Henna-coloured like a bride's hands.

The time of fire is past and gone
Instead of its flames come the flames of the tulips.
Oh thou, who has robbed the rose of its colour and its perfume,
Colour for the cheeks, perfume for the hair.
When thou bathest thy visage in the stream, it becomes
Tinted with the colour of the rose.
When thou combest thy hair, the whole hill is scented with
musk.

How can these lines be reconciled with the words of the French orientalist, G. Darmesteter, who mentions that Rudagi came blind into the world and possessed only of his 'Inner Eye' (*Luhah al-albah)*?

'But this vision was so clear that we often begin to doubt the reliability of the legend' (that he was born blind). 'In what has survived of his poetry colours play so surprisingly great a role that it seems to us Radagi forgets his blindness too easily.'

No, no one is so sensitive who has never seen the light of this world, the combinations of colour, the varied hues, the different tints and shades, the transparency, the glitter and the reflections. It is quite apparent that Rudagi in his childhood, in his youth and even in his mature age, must have been able to see.

Why then do the tenth- and eleventh-century poets write that Rudagi was blind? Abu Ali Mohammed ibn Ahmed Dakii Balchi, Muammari, Firdusi, and Nasiri Chuarav were not only familiar with Rudagi's verse but also, it would seem, possessed biographical data about him. Perhaps in his later years Rudagi really was blind?

In fact in many of Rudagi's later poems there is a complete lack of visual images and colours. The world around him finds expression only in perception through touch, odours and hearing.

When Rudagi speaks now of wine he no longer describes its colour, its sparkle in the glass, but he finds in it new qualities.

> Wine reveals man's nobility of soul,
> Wine distinguishes the upright from the infamous.

Even verses to the Beauties are devoid of the familiar colours.

> Priceless the sugar of their lips.
> From the looks wafts a musk-scented zephyr,
> From the tresses a light breath of rose perfume.
>
> With an apple I could compare her
> velvet-soft chin,
> But musk-scented apples are known in no land.

Obviously these lines come from a poet who had already lost the ability to visualise images. The physiological explanation for this is that after Rudagi lost his sight he reacted to his surroundings in a new way and tried to depict them in new images. We have here given only a few examples to illustrate our line of thought.

It is noteworthy that Rudagi's poems in which colours and visible images are lacking make a deeper impression, they are no doubt the work of a more mature man. Some of them have the character of ironical instructions while others again express the bitterness of disillusionment.

A small poem of Rudagi gives, in our opinion, an explanation of the circumstances of the sudden loss of his sight. The fact firmly expressed in this poem is so important that it merits a special, thorough-going examination. We cannot give here such an analysis and will just confine ourselves to a reproduction of the text:

> 'Oh Fair One, I heard that in days of suffering and release, Yusuf the Fair, in his life lost three shirts. One was through conspiracy steeped in blood, another torn in pieces through calumny, while the scent of the third made Yakub's weeping eyes to see. My face is like the first, my heart is like the second. May my fate be like the third.'

This poem offers a proof that Rudagi had been the victim of a horrible crime. These verses ring like a complaint of the poet concerning the outrages suffered by him and his dreadful punishment. He was calumniated, deceived and blinded.

Often the poem of the Three Shirts is regarded as an indication that Rudagi's sight was impaired by an advanced stage of cataract. However, it is certain that in Rudagi's days cataract, in the East, was successfully operated on, so Rudagi had the possibility of regaining his sight through an operation.

Furthermore one asks oneself what the references to deceit, calumny, a tormented heart and a visage streaming with blood mean that lend these verses so tragical a significance.

Unfortunately we know nothing about this period of Rudagi's

life which obviously he could only later write about. We must understand from the purely psychological point of view that the blinded poet at first avoided visible pictures, and then was quite naturally once more seized with new perceptions and feelings. It was at this period that he obtained that 'Inner Eye' his contemporaries ascribed to him.

If then it should be verified that the poet was violently deprived of his sight and our suppositions are correct, then effects on the organism must have been visible and the longer the time which elapsed between the loss of sight and Rudagi's death, so also the more marked the evidence of Rudagi's sufferings. We mean by this complicated, compensatory modifications in the whole body consequent upon the loss of sight, modifications which must have been produced in the skull and perhaps elsewhere in the skeleton.

Therefore it was extremely important to determine such individual peculiarities; they could not only serve to identify the skeleton but they could also facilitate the reconstruction of the poet's documentary portrait.

The 'Ode to Old Age'—one of Rudagi's last works—indicates not only that the poet was blind but that he had been blinded by an act of violence.

'But his trusted friends did not behave as the Emir ordered'—this brief allusion reflects sharply the tragical position into which the calumniated, dishonoured and blinded poet fell.

If we turn back again to the first lines of this poem:

My teeth are all damaged and fallen out,
. . . .
Now not one of them remains, they were damaged and fell
out.

In the original text Rudagi uses the word *furureht* which means literally 'fell out all at once'.

This evidence from Rudagi himself is of the greatest significance for us. For an adult man, indeed, there is no regular sequence for the loss of remaining teeth. With each individual they fall out at different times and only very rarely all at once. However, in the case of certain diseases (stomatitis, pyorrhea, scurvy, dystrophia from starvation) which are accompanied by damage to the gums, all the teeth are occasionally lost at one and the same time.

They get loose and fall out intact. This happens first of all with teeth which have only one root, thus with the incisors and canines; but occurs less often with the molars. These even with older men usually do not fall out. Generally the alveolar margin disappears. The body of the lower jaw seems to become thinner and rounded while in the upper jaw the gums lose almost all their thickness and are flattened down.

In his Ode Rudagi makes no mention of hunger or disease. Indeed, it may be noted that the poet was an unusually healthy man. In allegorical fashion he expresses this thus:

What sort of calamity? Perhaps a calamity of Saturn?
No, not a calamity of Saturn and not the long-lasting destiny.
What was it? I will tell thee, it was divine Providence.

If Rudagi had really suffered from a disease of the teeth he would have lost them gradually—and the first lines of the Ode would be pointless.

With simultaneous loss of all the teeth the obliteration of the sockets takes place also almost simultaneously. The alveolar margin of both jaws soon forms a ridge that is almost of the same height for all its length and shows an even or nearly even surface.

Therefore it could be clearly recognised that the first lines of the Ode might be a key for the identification of Rudagi's skeleton and I reported on the results of my investigations into the autobiographical details in Rudagi's work at a special meeting of the Rudagi jubilee committee and of the Tadjikstan authors' association on 20th November 1956.

I wanted to undertake the reconstruction of Rudagi's portrait only if the results of the investigations corresponded exactly with the characteristics we had defined.

A small jubilee committee expedition arrived in the village of Panjrud. It was composed of R. Amonov, folklorist and translator, V. Ranov, archaeologist, Machmudov, an authority on local history, and myself as scientific adviser. Machmudov was included because in 1940–1 he took part in the examination and excavation of a series of graves, in a search for Rudagi's burial-place.

On 23rd November 1956 at 1 p.m. the expedition reached Panjrud. The local population welcomed us heartily. They chatted in lively fashion about matters concerned with the proposed excavations. They all agreed that the blind musician Rudagi died and was buried in Panjrud though no man knew where his grave was.

When I visited the graveyard a small strip of it on the side of a hill attracted my attention. This terrain was bounded on the one side by the bed of a stream and on the other side by a low earthen wall. Behind was, on a lower level, the flattened surface of an ancient, neglected garden. The ground was thickly strewn with old grave-mounds.

One of the local inhabitants, an educated man called Mulloniso Bazarov who knew his literature and was an excellent gardener told us (through Amonov) that he remembered a tale recounted by his grandfather that above the blind poet's grave there was a tomb directly behind the garden-wall but naturally he could not indicate the exact spot. Bazarov's story was confirmed by Abdusator Amurov, Nasreddin Sakidov and a number of others. But the oldest of them, a man of at least sixty years of age, could not remember having seen a *Mazar*. He had however heard talk of one by very old men who had told stories about the blind Tadjik singer.

Rudagi died in disgrace and it is doubtful whether his admirers were able to put a monumental mausoleum over his grave; it is more probable that they built a small *Mazar* of brick, but the burial ground showed no traces of it.

When I had walked all over the cemetery I went back to the oldest part and to a small level space about nine feet square orientated to the cardinal points. The longer I considered this area the more I was convinced that the site was the only one which might have served as the foundation of a *Mazar*.

Indeed, I got the impression from the inhabitants' attitude that this spot had always been regarded as that of Rudagi's grave, therefore although the graveyard was overcrowded no interments were made there.

What we had to do first of all was to make sure that this burial-place really was that of Rudagi. If it was not then there would be no need to open it, but we could be sure only by examining the skull. So first of all we dug a broad path to the upper end of the area so as to be sure that we should come across the skull without disturbing the plan of the burial-chamber.

At a depth of 1·70 metres we came upon the skull which lay on its right side. While I was cleaning the facial skeleton my hands trembled with excitement. The silently waiting crowd seemed to notice my emotion. Then, suddenly, I felt a friendly hand on my shoulder while the hearty and fervent voice of an elderly man spoke to me. Amonov translated: 'You don't need to be perturbed, it is Rudagi, soon you will see his toothless mouth,' and in fact a few movements with a knife sufficed and then I glanced at both upper and lower jaw—they were entirely toothless. I got up from my knees. The men seemed as though freed from torpor. Amid a confusion of voices everyone appeared anxious to tell his neighbours something very quickly. What they were saying was so obvious that no interpreter was needed. As I knelt down again silence fell once more upon bystanders.

Finally the skull was cleaned. Yes, in all probability it was Rudagi's, but it was in bad condition, slightly bashed in, though not really deformed. The cheek-bone on the right side was broken, the whole upper jaw-bone broken also in the middle. The bones were damp and decayed, therefore they must be treated at once, in the grave itself there could be no question of doing this. The earth indeed was so wet that my knees were soaked although I had put down several thicknesses of newspaper. Common sense made it advisable to remove the skull from the grave. It was already about eight o'clock at night and in the mountains in November darkness falls abruptly with no twilight. So we decided to break our rule and to remove the skull without having first cleaned the whole skeleton. But there was another consideration. The skull, as I have said, was very poorly preserved and it was the object for which the whole excavation had been undertaken, so I must take no risks. In the grave it could suffer further damage since it was no longer supported by the earth which had surrounded it on all sides. The worst might happen, and this skull was not only of value for me but was a precious treasure for the people who had confided it to me. In order the better to determine the skull's position with regard to the whole skeleton I cleaned its upper part, that is to say, the collar-bones, the neck vertebrae and a portion of the shoulder-blades. It was then obvious that the corpse had been laid on its back, the left shoulder a little raised, the head resting on the right cheek and turned towards the direction of Mecca. It was thus a regular Moslem interment.

I removed the skull and mandible very carefully so that the place where they had lain remained undisturbed—that was very important since after they had been cleaned I wanted to put them back in their original position so that the remains could be photographed and described as a whole.

The bones were covered with paper and some earth sprinkled on it. I asked Machmudov to post a watchman at the grave all night. Holding the paper-wrapped skull in my hand and accompanied by the local inhabitants who had witnessed the excavation, I went off to the house of Nasr-ed-din Sckhidov who had most kindly put his dwelling at the disposal of the expedition. When I got into the courtyard of the house, it was night.

The village of Panjrud had its own generating station and all the houses and even the courtyard were lit up. I sought out a convenient corner. A lamp was hung above me so that I could set to work. I was practically left alone, only the old man stayed by my side. I was impressed by the tact of these people. I had hours of tiring work before me.

Before I soaked the skull in a preservative preparation I had to cleanse it thoroughly from the earth and as it was damp and brittle I feared that it might fall into pieces at the slightest movement. Inside the skull was a heavy, hard morsel of damp earth. Bit by bit I removed it with delicate instruments from the eye-sockets and the nasal opening as well as from the interior of the skull. I gathered the earth neatly together. When the old man saw I did not need it he gathered it up. When I asked him what he wanted to do with it he said, 'Take it back to the grave—that would be better. . . .'

It is useless to attempt the preservation of a damp skull. No adhesive will stick to the bones, therefore the skull must be thoroughly dried as soon as possible; to this end I bathed the cranium several times in alcohol at fifteen-minute intervals. After that the bones were treated with a very thin coating of Butvar (this is a patent artificial resin which can be recommended for the consolidation of wood, bones, textiles, clods of earth, etc.).

Twenty-five minutes later I repeated the Butvar treatment, but this time with a stronger solution, then after thirty minutes I applied another solution and finally after an hoür still another, the strength of the solution being increased each time. When the skull was dry it was painted with a thick layer of Butvar. By this treatment the bones of the facial skeleton which had become detached at the sutures fell into their original positions.

During the night of 24th November it snowed heavily. We were surrounded by a white coverlet. Even in the morning it was still snowing; however, we began at nine o'clock the clearing of the grave after a tent had been put up over it. In the spot where the sepulchre must have stood the earth was dug down to a depth of 40 centimetres and we found an oval-shaped broad space. At a depth of 70 centimetres appeared the remains of a wooden covering made of split and decayed thin planks of juniper-wood. The bad condition of this covering indicated that the grave was very ancient. Under the wooden cover lay the actual remains, the legs pointing towards the south. The grave was 1·90 metres long, and the bones were 1·70 metres below the surface of the ground. When the whole skeleton had been cleaned I replaced the skull and the lower jaw in their original positions. The impression of the skull could be clearly seen in the earth. The whole skeleton was then photographed.

The hands lay together in line with the elbows.

The shape of the grave and the presence of charcoal would alone be indications of great age and Professor M. J. Masson thinks that juniper-wood as well as the charcoal affords proof of a very ancient interment.

The skeleton was undoubtedly that of a man. The state of the skull and of the other bones indicated that the individual was aged at the time of his death. The ribs and backbone had been damaged, probably through some act of violence long before the death of the subject. The position of the bones at the base of the skull showed that the man habitually carried his head inclined backwards as blind men are accustomed to walk when they have no guide with them.

For a number of days I carried out preliminary examinations of the Panjrud skeleton. While studying the skull I noted various abnormalities in the formation of the upper margins of the eye-sockets which must have been directly due to the blinding.

Since the examination of the Panjrud remains revealed an extremely complicated set of compensatory changes, we decided that in making the portrait reconstruction we would reproduce the whole bust, so we built up the muscles layer by layer from the deepest. The skeleton in general indicated that the individual was well built and must have had lean muscles. The alterations due to old age in the skull showed that at the time of his death the man must have been at least seventy-eight or eighty.

In order to have an idea of the extent to which Rudagi's eyes were damaged we must try to imagine how he was blinded. In the East and in medieval times, blinding was an often inflicted punishment. Several methods seem to have been employed but those whereby the eye-ball was destroyed were the application of burning coals or gouging with a white-hot iron rod. The former method, by damaging the nerves, produced a partial change in the relief of the skull, but that of Panjrud showed nothing of this kind. Clearly, then, Rudagi was blinded by the second method which was the more usual.

Unfortunately there were no traces of hair or portions of clothing to be found with the Panjrud skeleton. It is, however, certain that elderly men in the tenth and eleventh centuries had their heads shaved smooth but wore both beards and moustaches.

The Tadjiks, especially the men, have generally thick, long eyebrows. The skull denoted clearly what was the racial type and like the Tadjiks in general, all Iranians have abundant growths of hair. The problem was to determine how men wore their beards in the tenth and eleventh centuries. Persian miniatures of the thirteenth to fifteenth centuries quite often depict older men with very large, bushy beards.

We were told that old men from the Samarkand and Bokhara area could still remember the time when it was forbidden to shave off beards. Today the town-dwelling Tadjiks usually have their beards shaved off or wear them cut very short. Naturally it would have been useless to try and discover valid fashion-laws for the whole Near East. It was better to restrict researches to one definite region—namely Rudagi's narrow homeland, that is to say the area where he was born, lived and died. Therefore we began our researches with Panjrud, his birthplace.

We noticed that the Tadjiks from the mountain villages had the biggest beards. Amonov told me that the Tadjiks in the hills still have bushy beards to this day and that formerly it was the custom that after a certain age the beard was not shaved.

The Tadjiks, have the strongest growth of beard of any of the peoples of the Soviet East; neither the Arabs, nor the Bokhara Jews, and still less the Turkomen and the Uzbeks, can boast of such fine and copious beards.

In agreement with A. A. Semenov, the poet Mirso Tursunzade and many other authorities on the Tadjik people, I gave Rudagi's bust a moderately full (for a Tadjik) beard, not very broad or long and with a drooping moustache.

The portrait was rounded off with a simple linen shirt next to the skin, an oriental mantle of coarse wool and a turban small but neatly wound around the head.

Can we now really assert that we found the remains of Rudagi? The following list of theories and established facts should not only answer this question but at the same time serve as a summary of what has gone before.

HYPOTHESIS	ESTABLISHED FACT
1 According to S. Aini's researches Rudagi's grave would be found in Panjrud.	1 The expedition excavated a grave in the village of Panjrud.
2 The poet's grave would lie at the corner of the garden.	2 The grave in question lay in the old graveyard behind the garden wall.
3 Over the grave a *Mazar,* an oriental funerary monument, must have been erected.	3 A levelled area of flat pounded clay facing the cardinal points and surrounded by a gutter would have served as the foundation for a former *Mazar*.

4 Rudagi was so highly regarded by the people that his *Mazar* could hardly have been used for another and later interment.	4 In the middle of the levelled clay area was found a grave with a skeleton.
5 There can be no doubt about Rudagi's sex.	5 The skeleton discovered was that of a male.
6 Rudagi was buried more than a thousand years ago.	6 The condition of the juniper wood cover indicates that the burial took place a very long time ago. Furthermore great antiquity is shown by some peculiarities in the construction of the grave.
7 The funerary rites must have been Moslem.	7 The interment showed indications of ancient Moslem rites.
8 Rudagi was aged at least 75 when he died.	8 The skeleton found belonged to a man who was at least 75–80 years old at his death.
9 A number of years before his death Rudagi had lost all his teeth.	9 The skull found at Panjrud was toothless.
10 Rudagi wrote that all his teeth fell out at one and the same time.	10 The skull in question showed (by the form of the alveolar margin of the jaws) that the teeth had indeed fallen out almost all at once.
11 Rudagi was not blind from birth.	11 The formation of the interior of the eye-sockets proved that the owner of the skull could not have been blind from birth.
12 Rudagi lost his sight when he was over 60.	12 The process of compensatory re-construction of the skull bones and the back-bone demanded several years before the skeleton finally found its definite constitution.
13 Rudagi was blinded several years before his death.	13 From the time that the man was blinded a number of years must have passed as the complicated compensatory changes in skull and skeleton indicate.

14 Rudagi was blinded so his skeleton must show traces of violence perpetrated on him.	14 The skeleton showed traces of violence. Part of the sacrum was damaged and three ribs were broken a number of years before the death of the individual. The ribs had knitted together during the subject's life-time.
15 The local inhabitants could not have forgotten the grave of their teacher Rudagi.	15 The fact that on the site of the *Mazar* no later burial took place is proof that the site was protected. It ranked as a holy place and was revered as the grave of the teacher Rudagi.

The above table shows clearly that the theory corresponds entirely with the facts. So the correctness of Idris Hafiz's testimony and its explanation by S. Aini about Rudagi's burial at Panjrud was proved. The biological-biographical clues in Rudagi's poetry are confirmed by the Panjrud skeleton. The reports by tenth- and eleventh-century poets that Rudagi was blind and our supposition that he was blinded when over sixty years of age were also confirmed.

Such a combination of circumstances can hardly be attributed to chance. We therefore felt ourselves justified in making a report that the skeleton found by the expedition on 23rd and 24th November 1956 at Panjrud really was that of the poet Rudagi.

Friedrich von Schiller

Friedrich von Schiller, the great German poet, dramatist and humanist was born on 10th November 1759 and died on 19th May 1805.

An extraordinary combination of circumstances led me to investigate Schiller's remains. He died in the prime of life after prolonged suffering. Before the burial a professor Jagemann painted a portrait of the poet on his death-bed while the sculptor Keller prepared two death-masks, one in terra-cotta and the other in plaster. Schiller's remains were then placed in a small tomb in the so-called *Kassengewölbe* at Weimar. Both masks were deposited in the Thuringian provincial library.

After his death Schiller's fame continued to increase. From far and wide admirers flocked to visit his tomb. The people of Weimar were overjoyed at the stream of visitors but they also began to feel somewhat ashamed that in a vault where many other persons had been interred Schiller's tomb did not occupy the place of honour that should have been accorded to it.

But more than twenty years passed by before in 1826 the then burgomaster of the town, one Schwabe, undertook, with Goethe's support, investigations to identify Schiller's remains. So as to arouse no opposition from his fellow-citizens, who might disapprove of the proceedings, Schwabe worked in the vault only at night and his task proved no easy one. There were by this time seventy-one bodies buried in one small vault. The coffins lay in several rows and piled up one on the top of the other. Many of them had rotted and there was a jumble of bones. In these circumstances the identification of Schiller's remains demanded not only energy and enterprise but also knowledge. This latter Schwabe certainly possessed for he had known Schiller well and remembered him distinctly. Still, he sought out various people who had been contemporaries of the poet and these included Schiller's servant Rudolf and also a coffin-maker. Several of these men gave clear descriptions of the writer. They recollected his smile and his very fine teeth with peculiar striations on the enamel.

The coffin-maker declared that Schiller was a tall man and a prominent citizen known all over the town. Rudolf reported that about a year before his death Schiller had had a tooth drawn but that otherwise his teeth were in perfect condition.

For five nights Schwabe searched for the poet's bones. On the last night, when he was nearly exhausted, he uncovered twenty-five skulls all at once. He left the lower jaws on one side; he was certain he could recognise from the dentition which skull belonged to which skeleton and so in this way discover the original emplacement. He examined the skulls by daylight and one of them he identified as that of the poet. Then he sought for the lower jaw belonging to the skull and which displayed the characteristic dentition of Schiller. Goethe took part in the identification. The skeleton was then placed in the grand-ducal library and under Goethe's personal protection. At this time a plaster-cast was also made. In 1827 Schiller's mortal remains were solemnly transferred to the so-called *Fürstengruft* of the Grand-Duke Karl August of Saxe-Weimar.

Half a century later the noted anatomist Welcker (then renowned for his having compared two skulls with Raphael's self-portrait and for having determined which of the two was the right one) decided to examine the Schiller skull and to check whether the identification had been rightly made. He compared the plaster cast of the skull with the plaster death-mask and declared that the skeleton found in 1826 could not be that of Schiller, since the profiles of mask and skull had not the same contour. So arose unexpectedly a discussion in which many anatomists took part.

In 1911 the anatomist Froriep, who had adopted Welcker's opinion, undertook to open the tomb. Surprisingly enough he came to the conclusion that the plaster cast could not be admitted as evidence since it was larger than the original and was indeed a 'gigantic' mask. So he decided on the terra-cotta death-mask as the standard for a test. He then discovered in the original vault a skull which in all the main measurements corresponded with the terra-cotta death-mask of Schiller.

At the anatomical congress held in Munich in 1911 Froriep presented the skull (evidently a copy) and sought to persuade those present that it was really that of the poet. A year later the anatomist Neuhauss denied this. The skull Froriep found obviously could not be ascribed to Schiller since it possessed what were clearly female characteristics.

The discussion now took a new turn. There were two skulls each of which it was claimed was that of Schiller. Which of them was the right one was very hard to say. Nevertheless, the tendency was —obviously from habit—to give the preference to the skull found in 1826. It was placed in a red sarcophagus and laid next to Goethe's remains in the central portion of the *Fürstengruft*. This casket attracted the attention of the poet's admirers and on it flowers for Schiller were laid.

The German Academy of Sciences in Berlin invited me to go to Weimar in 1961: there I was to endeavour by my method of plastic reconstruction to identify which was Schiller's skull. I am most grateful to the Academy for this proof of trust in my method.

The journey to Weimar naturally caused me a good deal of excitement. I knew Welcker's work well and, for me, he counted as an infallible authority. So the skull discovered in 1826 could not be Schiller's. Froriep, it is true, had compared the skull he had discovered in 1911 with the terra-cotta death-mask, but I had known since I was a child that terra-cotta when baked loses about one-tenth of its volume. If the measurements of Froriep's specimen corresponded with those of the mask, then that skull could not be Schiller's. Therefore, I must get the now completely ruined vault cleared for the third time—and without any assurance that I should light upon the real Schiller skull.

As generally happens, there were plenty of surprises. When the red sarcophagus containing the 1826 skeleton was opened I felt at once reassurred. There before me lay, in anatomical connection, the skeleton of a very tall man. A rapid glance was enough to leave no doubt that the skull, the lower jaw and the remaining bones all belonged to one individual. The skull was particularly striking, I may almost say beautiful—a magnificent forehead, large eye-orbits, strongly projecting nasal bones, fine, regular teeth. This corresponded with the outward appearance of the poet, and I could not put the thought from my mind that Welcker must have made a mistake. But how was that possible? Indeed how was it even thinkable?

The second tomb with the remains of the skeleton found in 1911 was also opened. It struck me at once that the various bones did not belong together, they differed in size, in age and in sex. No doubt the remains of several persons had been collected together. Especially noticeable was the incongruity between skull and lower jaw. The latter was very large and must have come from an individual of at least sixty to sixty-five years of age. The teeth were quite worn down. The skull itself was quite small, had a nose not at all prominent and possessed a row of irregular prognathous teeth. It was unmistakably the skull of a woman. She was obviously very young, just about twenty years old when she died.

How was it possible that an anatomist of Froriep's rank could have taken so clearly marked a female skull for that of a man? How was it that he had not remarked on a difference of more than twenty years between this female skull and Schiller's? How was it possible that disparity between the contour of the death-mask and that of this female skull had not been rightly appreciated? All this will always remain a mystery for me. I could not understand how Froriep so stoutly and obstinately maintained his diagnosis when he had been made aware of his mistake. Furthermore his whole method for identification was erroneous. The terra-cotta death-mask was smaller than life-size and the skull was that of a woman not of a man, while the age of this woman must be set at about twenty and not forty-six years.

In one case there was the skeleton of a very tall man showing traces of serious disease—tuberculosis. In the other case there was a jumble of remains from several different individuals of various ages and sizes.

Once it had been identified as that of a woman the 1911 skull could be disregarded. Nevertheless, I decided, so that this skull should never again be taken into consideration, to prepare from the head the pattern of this unknown young woman's profile. I drew the skull with a dioptograph and then reconstituted on paper the design of the face. As might have been expected the drawing showed nothing like Schiller's characteristic profile. My picture was that of a woman with a small, slightly tip-tilted nose and a projecting upper lip. Then I considered I had done everything necessary to prove that the 1911 skull could not be that of Schiller. It now remained to be seen whether the skull found by Schwabe in 1826 really was Schiller's and if this was so, how Welcker could have made his mistake.

In order to identify the skull I had to reconstruct one half of the head. That would be enough for a comparison with the plaster death-mask and for proof of the reconstruction's objectivity. The death-mask was to serve as test-piece. I was not familiar with the mask and had in fact never seen it. I had no portrait of Schiller with me. But it might be objected, 'We are dealing with Schiller, how is it possible not to know his appearance?" Quite right. It was not all that difficult to create a model of the poet's well-known face. But my task was quite a different one.

During the whole of my work I had my pupils and colleagues Dr. H. Ullrich and the interpreter Stephan at my side. What I had to do was to furnish the skull with the estimated thickness of soft parts and then according to the form of the head to build up and reproduce definite morphological details of the face. This must be carried out on one half of the skull so that the process could be followed and an objective check made possible. If the skull came from another person than Schiller then it must, because of the construction of its peculiar details, reveal other facial features than Schiller's. Any attempt to produce subjectively the size, the thickness of the soft parts, the shape and the facial features would at once result in an incongruity between the skull and the reconstructed face. Only Schiller's authentic skull could produce a portrait that was recognisably his.

Furthermore, for a comparison between the mask and the reconstructed head, the peculiarities of the face had to be taken into account and of these (asymmetry, measurements, proportions of facial details, etc.) I had naturally no idea at all. I must create no abstract type but a quite individual visage. And, again the measurements had to coincide and these could not just be guessed.

No sooner had I traced the medium ridge than my colleagues there recognised the profile of the poet. During the reconstruction work I had also another surprise. The skull displayed a considerable degree of projection in profile, a marked development of the nasal bones, and a considerable vertical projection of the orbits and cheek-bones. Generally speaking such a skull-construction indicates a strongly marked nose-lip furrow. In the present case, however, this complex was such that morphological details escaped me and afforded no evidence for the depiction of these generally very marked facial lines. In all my long years of practice this was the first time that, in the reconstruction of a face of a man of more than forty years of age, I found no clues for the indication of this characteristic and yet always individual facial fold. Such a form of cheek is even in children a great rarity. It was only after many attempts that I undertook to depict the nose-lip fold although I much feared

I was making a mistake. I said to my colleagues even, 'The morphological peculiarities of the skull offer no possibility for representing the nose-lip line. Either we have here an extraordinarily rare and individual peculiarity, or I am overlooking something and am making a big mistake.'

When the reconstruction was completed, then it must be compared with the mask and this comparison took place at an official festival occasion. In the presence of collaborators from the Pre- and Proto-history Museum in Weimar, of its director Dr. Behm-Blancke and of Dr. Ullrich, the plaster-cast and my reconstruction were placed opposite one another. The reconstructed half-face undoubtedly looked like the death-mask. So the skull was that of Schiller. There were the same details of nose and mouth, and also the same form of the cheeks without a nose-lip line. The symmetrical shape of the mouth was astonishingly similar. The main difference between the two visages was due to the fact that I had modelled a 'living' face. This was seen not only by the open eyes, but also by the obviously 'living' muscles which seemed not to have lost their tonicity. The death-mask on the other hand reflected the whole condition of a dead man's markedly altered visage.

I drew the attention of those present to the defects present in the death-mask. It had obviously not been prepared by a very experienced person and displayed many technical shortcomings. And then I realised the reason for Welcker's error. Before placing the mass of plaster on Schiller's head the sculptor had wrapped it round with a piece of stuff so as not to spoil the hair. Traces of the wrapping and of the knot holding it together could clearly be seen on the hinder part of the cast. When the mask was ready the sculptor removed the marks of the wrapping and in scraping off the plaster he altered the contour of the head.

Welcker when identifying mask and skull had taken care to compare the contours of the head and the skull-cap which were much alike, but as the contour of the mask had been distorted naturally the outlines did not correspond. Welcker, who clearly was not acquainted with the technique of mask-modelling, could not imagine that it was distorted.

The reconstructed half-head was absolutely true to Schiller's portrait and displayed even the finest details of his visage. Later, when I had returned to Moscow I repeated the reconstruction process on a splendid cast of the Schiller skull which had been prepared for me by the Museum for Pre- and Proto-history. I wanted to re-create the real visage of the poet as an object for comparison with the imperfect mask. So this time I modelled the poet's face with closed eyes as though he were lying on his death-bed. So I was able to represent the striking, harmonious beauty of his visage in a state of complete repose.

The countenance thus revealed was one of inner significance . . . the slight asymmetry of the mouth with the ghost of a smile lent the face a certain mildness. It was truly the visage of a poet and humanist.

The portrait prepared from the skull in May 1963 was presented by the U.S.S.R. Academy of Sciences to the German Democratic Republic and may be seen today in the *Schillerhaus* at Weimar.

Ivan the Terrible, Tsar Ivan IV (1530–1584), son of Basil III

On 23rd April 1953 a special commission from the Ministry of Culture of the U.S.S.R. under the direction of Professor A. N. Smirnov, opened the sarcophagus of Tsar Ivan IV in the Moscow Kremlin's Archangel Cathedral. The object of the undertaking was to carry out scientific and historical investigations.

The tombs of Tsar Ivan IV and of his sons—the Tsarevich (Crown Prince) Ivan Ivanovich, and the Tsar Feodor Ivanovich—were of brick and bore epitaphs. The monuments were covered with plaster and from the details of their construction the chronological order of the burials could be determined. So, for instance, it could be seen that for the interment of Feodor Ivanovich, the tomb which had been previously erected for the Tsarevich Ivan Ivanovich was chiselled back. After the burial of Tsar Feodor both monuments were plastered over. Much later on all three tombs were overlaid with bronze as were all the tombs in the Archangel Cathedral. The condition of the plaster layer and of the brickwork showed that the graves had never been disturbed.

During the clearing of the graves every precaution was taken to see that the brickwork of the monuments should remain as intact as possible. With this object cross-trenches were dug and the upper walls so to speak suspended in the air by means of wooden and metal struts. In this way the lower parts of the tombs were taken to pieces so that their original appearance could be restored after the sarcophagi had been opened.

These operations showed that the graves lay on the level of the old wooden flooring upon which the slabs of the sarcophagi rested, but protected by a rather thick layer of sand which prevented their being damaged during the building of the brick tombs, whose walls bore down on the slabs' edges.

The Tsar lay in a white stone sarcophagus. His skeleton was partially covered with torn pieces of a monk's garment. Over the head and masking the face were the remnants of a monk's cowl and a filet on which were embroidered texts of prayers. On the breast lay a monk's apron top embroidered with the scene of the crucifixion on Golgotha. On a level with the head and to the left side was a goblet of dark-blue glass enamelled in yellow.

The skeleton was on his back and the skull turned slightly towards the left. The right arm was sharply flexed at the elbow and its hand touched the chin. The left arm was also bent at a right angle so that forearm and hand lay diagonally across the breast. The skeleton was in good state of preservation although the base of the skull and the right temporal bone were completely destroyed. The skull-bones moreover were very brittle. On the face, here and there, could be seen a few small hairs of the eyebrows and beard.

The Research Institute of Forensic Medicine undertook a chemical investigation of the remains and this revealed traces of arsenic and quicksilver. The arsenic was present to the extent of 8–193 microgrammes (–gamma) and so came within the normal. The mercury content, however, was 20–1393 microgrammes per 100 grammes of material tested. The presence of such a large quantity of mercury demands an explanation.

The anthropological examination of the bones was carried out by Professor G. F. Debez. The type of Ivan IV's skull approximated to the Dinaric. The high eye-orbits and the markedly jutting, fine nose, however, seemed to indicate a Mediterranean influence which can be explained by the Tsar's pedigree. His grandmother Sophia Palaeologa was, as is well known, of Greek origin.

The Tsar was a tall man (1·80 metres or nearly 6 feet), well developed, in his youth strong, but towards the end of his life apparently very fat. He weighed over 95 kilogrammes (about 210 pounds).

Owing to disturbances in his metabolism he suffered quite early some ossification of the cartilages and of several ligaments, and in nearly all the bones there was evidence of osteophytes. The joints of the long bones showed traces of an inflammatory process —poly-arthritis. The cartilages of the breast-bones and the larynx were ossified and well preserved. All these indications show that Ivan suffered from constant pain that sometimes appears to have been very severe. As a result he had to pay great attention to his health and take great care of himself. In public he often sat on an armchair with a straight back. We know that he often had himself carried in a chair from one apartment to another. As a result he gradually lost still further his power of movement.

A radiographical examination of the skeleton was undertaken and anthropologists, anatomists, radiologists, stomatologists and experts in forensic medicine took part in the examination of the remains. There was no great difference of opinion among them. Thus an almost concordant report was produced.

The skeleton of Ivan the Terrible showed no signs of any congenital pathology, nor of any symptoms of disease of the bones. There was however one marked anomaly—the exceedingly late change in dentition. To judge from the degree of wear of the teeth, incisors, canines and premolers erupted only after his fiftieth year. Also the peculiar form of the breast-bone with the projecting xiphoid process must be accounted an anomaly. This provided a clear indication of the configuration of the thorax in the region of the belly.

Among the pathological changes in the skeleton may be mentioned a pronounced torsion of the sternum. On the whole skeleton an ossification of the cartilages and ligaments was noticeable which probably was accompanied by an arthorosis. The Tsar must have suffered from poly-arthritis as could be seen from traces of deforming spondylosis in the whole skeleton. It is clear Ivan the Terrible suffered from severe metabolic disturbances and these were due to his way of life. The absolute lack of a regular daily programme, immoderate indulgence in alcohol and over-eating were the main causes of his sufferings, of his early senility and of his death. The presence of mercury in his organism is certainly to be attributed to his use of mercury ointment to alleviate the pains in his limbs.

And now I had to reconstruct the portrait of Ivan IV from his bones.

During the course of years many popular legends grew up around the figure of Ivan the Terrible. His *persona* has preoccupied historians, publicists, dramatists, poets, painters and actors. But what has aroused this wide-spread interest in the personality of the monarch? What excited the imaginations of people of the most various sorts?

By a comparison of all the descriptions of the Tsar's appearance as recorded by his contemporaries, with the interpretation of these data by historical students, a more or less concordant representation of the Tsar's visage was produced. This picture however could not rank as wholly reliable and precise enough. The spiritual world of Ivan the Terrible was so varied and so contradictory that one is inclined to reject the objectivity of these descriptions.

In the twelfth year before his death (1572) the Tsar in his Will gave this relentless character-sketch of himself:

> 'My understanding was infamous and my spirit corrupt, so also my mind was defiled by a liking for unworthy things, my mouth by words of murder, lewdness and other bad acts, my tongue by self-praise, my throat and chest by pride and arrogance, my hands by indecent contacts, by theft and assassination, my inner urge by shamelessness, debauchery and drinking, my belly by grave offences of the flesh and a readiness to commit all sorts of evil. . . '
>
> (From I. A. Soloviov, *Ivan Grozny*, 1898.)

This self-accusation clearly rings true. It is not by chance that at one and the same time mention is made of the Tsar's greatness and futility, of his sagacity and narrowmindedness. But however we may judge him and whatever we may say about him Ivan IV was undoubtedly a most remarkable and outstanding personage.

Many people believe that the unbalanced and unrestrained elements in Ivan the Terrible's character can be attributed to his ancestry. Others say they were caused by his upbringing which favoured every kind of cruelty and obstinacy. Although it is not our task here to fathom or to vindicate the complicated nature of Ivan the Terrible, it is difficult to free oneself completely from the traditional stories. How can we forget the portraits made by Repin and Antokolski? However, these pictures must be excluded from the imagination of the researcher who wants to create the authentic figure of the Tsar.

In order to free myself from the numerous representations of the Tsar I chose deliberately a more complicated technique than usual in my reconstruction work. After a thorough examination of the skeleton's peculiarities and after mounting the upper part of the torso, I lighted upon a series of individual characteristics which led me away from the traditional picture. All the pictures of later ages show Ivan as thin, wasted away, an asthetic man. The skeleton however proves that Ivan must have been stoutly built, and as I have mentioned, towards the end of his life, fat. Because of the condition of the bones the reconstruction had to be made on a plaster cast. The skull, the lower jaw, the upper part of the torso and the shoulder-bones were reconstructed. Then I reconstituted the deep-lying muscles of the neck and head. The whole process was filmed and preserved in pictures.

The most revealing portrait was that of the face without any hair. It seemed to hide nothing—the form of the low forehead, the peculiarities of the supraorbital area, the size and outline of the symmetrical orbits conditioned the external specific appearance of the eyes. The mouth with its drooping corners and expression of disgust was determined by the shape of the dentition. The face was hard, commanding, undoubtedly clever but cruel and unpleasing with pendulous nose and clumsy chin. The lower lip was indicated by the occlusion of the teeth and the face was set off by a powerful neck and a massive, well-filled torso.

The hair I arranged after pictures of Basil III and Ivan IV and the clothing from fragments we found in the grave of Tsar Feodor Ivanovich.

The portrait reconstructed from the skull agrees entirely with the descriptions his contemporaries gave of the appearance of Tsar Ivan IV.

Tsar Feodor Ivanovich (1557–1598), son of Ivan the Terrible

The sarcophagus of Tsar Feodor Ivanovich was opened on 2nd June 1963. It was of white stone and covered with a massive slab on which was the following inscription:

> 'On the sixth day of the month of January in the year 1598 and in the night from Friday to Saturday, there departed from us with the holy blessing of God and of our Lord and Saviour Jesus Christ, the pious and most Christian Lord Tsar and Great Prince Feodor Ivanovich. Monarch of all Rus. His mortal remains were interred on the eighth of January.'

In the sarcophagus the body lay under a damask coverlet, clad in a long robe and bound round with a cord. At the right elbow there was a transparent greenish-glass vessel. The skeleton lay on its back. The legs were outstretched and the arms crossed over the breast, but the remains were in a bad state of preservation. Of the head only the face and fragments of the lower jaw survived. A few of the beard hairs and several strands of hair from the back of the head were visible. The hair was not very long (from 5 to 6 centimetres, say 2 to 2½ inches) and rather wavy but as it was depigmented it was difficult to determine what its original colour had been. However, to all appearances, Tsar Feodor must have had light brown hair with reddish glints in it. The long bones of the arms and legs as well as the bones of the feet were well preserved but the whole region of the breast and backbone was completely destroyed. It was noteworthy that some finger- and toenails had remained intact. They were well formed and very neatly pared.

The chemical examination of the remains was undertaken by the Institute for Forensic Medicine Research. There was present in them arsenic in quantities from 10 to 80 microgrammes and mercury in amounts of from 3 to 333 microgrammes in each 100 grammes of the specimens examined. Since no evidence of poisoning could be deduced from this, the cause of the Tsar's death remains undetermined.

Feodor Feodorovich's bones were thoroughly examined by experts. The anthropological investigation was undertaken by the Laboratory for Plastic Reconstruction. G. F. Debez personally took part in the work. From the anthropological point of view the skeleton's type certainly approximated to the Dinaric. The skull resembled that of Ivan IV and presented a similar asymmetry and the same anomaly of the late eruption of the teeth. The forehead was, however, more lofty than that of Ivan the Terrible, the supraorbital area was smaller but the very narrow and the delicately formed nose projected even more markedly. Tsar Feodor was a small man (about 1·60 metres or 5 feet 3 inches tall). His skeleton showed no traces of pathological conditions or of disease which might have caused alterations in the bones; neither could any senile changes be observed. His apparent 'biological' age corresponded clearly with that given in the records.

The absence of the greater part of the skull-vault, of the neck bones and most of those of the breast and the fragmentary condition of the upper part of the torso limited the possibilities for reconstruction. So I was able to reconstitute only the face and not the whole head.

A seventeenth-century portrait, by an unknown artist, gave an indication of the Tsar's way of wearing his hair.

When I had finished my work I consulted several descriptions of Feodor Ivanovich left by his contemporaries. They describe him as quite different from Ivan the Terrible. Giles Fletcher, the envoy of Queen Elizabeth I of England at Feodor's court, gives an account of the Tsar as 'small and plump and inclined to dropsy, sluggish . . . and always smiling . . . he seems feeble-minded . . . but kindly . . . and exceedingly superstitious'.

The appearance of Feodor's reconstituted face fully confirms Fletcher's character-sketch. When I compared the reconstruction with the seventeenth-century portrait I noticed so many points of resemblance that one could almost believe that the picture was wrongly dated and was painted from life—or at least that the portrait was a copy of an earlier one made in the lifetime of Feodor Ivanovich.

Now, a whole series of portraits of historical personages has been laid before the reader. These are personages dating from various epochs and they are of varying anthropological types, of different age-groups and constitutional characteristics. For some of them no information was available, whereas for others there were paintings and sculptures representing them as they appeared in life.

All the faces we have portrayed show the specific traits of the individual although in every case the skull alone served as the foundation for the reconstructions. These are authentic documents and not the product of our fancy's subjective promptings, they are indeed reliable interpretations of information afforded by the human skull.

Index